Helping Children
Overcome Fear in a Medical Setting

A Guide for Healthcare Professionals

Rob Luka, R.N., C.Ht.

THE WELLNESS TRAINING CENTER
LEICESTER, NORTH CAROLINA

Published by The Wellness Training Center
Suite A, P.O. Box 599
Leicester, NC 28748

ISBN-10: 0-9794516-0-4
ISBN-13: 978-0-9794516-0-7
LCCN: 2007924873

For additional copies or to contact the author, visit www.RobLuka.com.

Credits

Excerpt from *A Return to Love* used by permission of Marianne Williamson.

Chapter Two: Comments on John Dennis taken from "Voice of the Diabetic" — interview by Ed Bryant, Volume 18, No. 4

"Transformation" in Chapter Three: Copyright © Osho International Foundation, Switzerland, www.osho.com. Taken from The Osho Transformation Tarot, St. Martin's Press, New York, NY. ISBN 0312245300. Used by permission of Osho International Foundation.

DENNIS THE MENACE ® used by permission of Hank Ketcham Enterprises and © North American Syndicate.

Illustrations in Chapter Thirteen from *Diabetes Care for Babies, Toddlers, and Preschoolers,* Copyright © 1999 by Jean Betschart. Reprinted with permission of John Wiley and Sons, Inc.

Book design: Janice M. Phelps, www.janicephelps.com

*I dedicate this book to all those
who touch the lives
of our blessed children.*

Table of Contents

Understanding your own response when faced with a frightened child. How you respond influences the direction a child's fear will take. The mirror technique. Fear changes shape. Recognize and use the power of your own authority.

What the mind believes tends to be realized. The expectations you create determine outcomes. A child shares his positive experience in his own words. People never forget you when you empower them. Find your confidence in creating positive expectations. Key moments to look for as opportunities to shift a child's expectations in a positive direction.

The intention you carry has a powerful effect on yourself and those around you. Intention comes naturally. How to bring your intention alive. Children naturally sense and respond to a loving intention. Statements of intention. Practicing intentional listening. Atisha's exercise.

Rapport creates an extraordinary connection to children. A three-year-old's response to rapport. How to create instant rapport with children. How to create instant rapport with adults. Never underestimate the power of rapport.

"Fear and pain need not overcome our children in a medical setting."

Foreword

Pain is universal. All creatures with even the most primitive nervous systems will react to stimulation that threatens their comfort. Our own sense of when we hurt speaks to the prevalence of pain and the desire to avoid it. Countless dollars are spent to relieve pain, and millions of people are chronic victims of their own nervous system's vigilance to unwanted pressures.

The basic purpose of pain is to protect. In spite of that, we know that pain also evokes fear, anxiety and the ever-mounting presence of stress. This is true for all of us. But pain cannot always be avoided. The reasons for this are multiple. When pain must be faced, every effort to cope, especially release from fear, must be sought.

That is why this book is so important. Adults may have sufficient understanding to deal with their pain, their fear, and their apprehension, no matter the source. Children do not have that level of sophistication. In these pages, Rob Luka deals with the fear children have as they face the pain and the fear of medical treatment. The personal stories and the practical suggestions illustrate the significance of addressing fear and pain in children and point to the positive outcomes, which result. This book is a vital tool for those who deal with children in fearful settings. It is a must-read for parents and caregivers who must help children cope with their fear, and it is a must-read for all those who set up the institutions of healing.

Fear and pain need not overcome our children in a medical setting. That is the ultimate message of this book. Read it now so that message may become your own.

Olson Huff, MD
Founding Medical Director, Mission Children's Hospital
Asheville, North Carolina
Fellow, American Academy of Pediatrics

*Open your heart here, as widely
as you would open your mind in
the most prestigious school of learning.*

Introduction

*S*omewhere along the line in my thirty-year nursing career, I became filled with a passion. A passion to see to it that the children I worked with had a positive experience during their medical procedures, no matter how afraid they initially appeared. Throughout those years, I found it increasingly difficult to accept the fear children expressed in any medical environment as a natural or necessary element. Seeing kids paralyzed by fear made me determined to find a better way. Gradually, I created an approach I was comfortable with that readily eased children's fears and caught the attention of my peers and coworkers, who asked for guidance. This approach is the foundation for the creation of this book.

Working with frightened children didn't always come easy, however. The first time I had to administer an intramuscular injection to a child, it was a painful experience. Careerwise I was still young and inexperienced not only with children, but with all my patients. The doctor ordered 25 mg of Demerol for a seven-year-old I was caring for in an outpatient setting. Back then with controlled substances you had to get the keys to the medicine cart, unlock it in the presence of another nurse, then do a count together to ensure security with narcotics and, finally, record the patient's name. After this, and with medication in hand, I nervously approached the room. The little girl looked at me, and then at the two-and-one-half-inch capped needle, and started screaming and crying while grabbing her mother, who looked scared too. So there we were, all three of us rapidly vibrating this energy of fear. I took a step closer and anxiously started to pull the red rubber needle cap off. Apparently, I was a lot more nervous than I realized at the time. Right in front of both of them, and in one quick motion, I pulled off the needle cap and shoved the entire two-and-one-half-inch exposed needle into and across the palm of my hand. My hand went numb. So did I as I turned around and left the room. Now I wanted to scream! The child stopped crying as I left, out of sheer confusion I imagine. I am sure it had nothing to do with her confidence in me. I do remember, however, going right back into the room (with a new syringe, of course) and giving that injection uneventfully. At least for her anyway. I still carry the ego wounds. There's a name for that kind of self-inflicted injury: embarrass-o-phobia. I don't remember the explanation I wrote on the narcotics sheet when I went back for a second dose of Demerol where it asked…"Reason for waste"!

Funny, that a guy like that ends up writing a book like this. I can recall my own reservations as a child about doctors, my fear of blood, and how the tiniest incident could get blown out of proportion. Eventually I grew out of those perceptions and was drawn to medicine and nursing — or more precisely, it was drawn to me.

My career began with my first job opportunity in high school as an orderly in a nursing home. Then I was offered a position as an orderly at Mercy Hospital in Buffalo, New York, when a scholarship for nursing school suddenly appeared shortly afterward. Due to my own childhood fears, I seemed to have a natural affinity to understand and console the sick and injured, and I felt comfortable when confronted with their apprehensions of being hospitalized.

I was fascinated to learn about human nature, psychology, and how different cultures perceive the mind and its natural tendencies. That fascination peaked when I met a gentleman who offered to use regression (to mentally go back in time) to help me understand a recurring nightmare I had experienced during my childhood. I was always curious as to the reason behind the same repetitious dream and what it was trying so hard to tell me. His compassion and abilities to help me understand those dreams made a tremendous impact, as it started my journey toward learning more about neurolinguistic programming, or NLP. This branch of psychology deals effectively with behavior modification and is highly interactive. I found it particularly interesting in how powerfully we can engage the mind to work for us in ways that improve our lives and change our perceptions of things we believe we can't change.

Introduction

Then I moved to India, and lived there for three months steeped in a culture of spiritual experience. It was the kindest gift I ever gave to myself and it was the type of journey I never could have imagined, in so many ways. One of which was learning how profoundly Eastern Indian culture has surpassed the rest of the world in its understanding of the human condition, the spiritual dimension, and the workings of the mind. It seems only logical that they would, since India is such a poor country with limited means, resources and technology. The people don't have an overabundance of material things to distract them from themselves. As a result, the culture has learned to move inward toward the deep exploration of subjectivity and the inner dimension of mind and spirit. Eastern Indians also express an uncanny ability to know fulfillment and a sense of peace in one's life that is so alive, active and vibrant amidst destitution and extreme poverty. It was here that I gained valuable insight into the habitual tendencies of the mind and its potential to break through and transform itself. Almost all of the new psychology of behavior modification that is taught in America today comes from ancient Eastern roots.

When I began working more closely with children in my career as a registered nurse, I could easily relate to their fear of medical procedures, and now I had the tools and skills to do something about it. My own experience as a child, my nurse's training, learning neurolinguistic programming, and the profound impact of India, seemed to combine into a sort of ready-mix formula. My passion became helping children shift from a state of fear into a position of empowerment by dismantling their fear and then helping them go through a medical procedure calmly. Over time, this became a natural approach.

Children in particular seemed to gravitate to and resonate with my ideas and suggestions. Using this approach always seemed to make it so much easier for them to shift gears on a moment's notice and try different ideas to conquer their self-defeating thoughts, fears and emotional obstacles. Adults too, but usually with a more sophisticated struggle, as if their fear was something too valuable to part with.

It was encouraging to me when many of my fellow nurses began to ask me the specifics of how I was approaching the kids. They started to notice that my interactions with children were frequently very positive and that there was less crying on the days I worked. It started to become a topic of conversation over lunch, and I was being consulted more frequently on how my colleagues could approach their own fearful patients to achieve the same results. Then one day I overheard two of my coworkers (all real names have been changed) discussing how they were going to work with a frightened and challenging nine-year-old in the Emergency Room who needed an intravenous line inserted. The child was overly anxious and hesitant to cooperate, and they were discussing different ways to approach him to avoid further upset. While they were engrossed in their conversation, I approached the child.

"Just a little pinch," I said, as I quickly and quietly inserted the needle in the boy's completely relaxed arm without him making a sound. Michelle and Tammy had just finished their conversation and were ready to get started when I came out of the room.

"It's already in," I told them.

Surprisingly, they looked at each other and then at me and said, "Teach us what you do with children." Requests for inservice training followed.

At the time, I didn't know how to respond. This was something expressed so naturally through me that breaking it down into structured steps and putting it into explainable and teachable pieces was something I had never thought about. It was awkward to explain. I also came to realize that this "whole approach" I was using far exceeded the sum of the individual parts and I found myself asking, how do I teach that? How do I teach the subtle, the intangibles? Michelle, Tammy, Mike, Dawn and others helped to start the journey of that explanation.

It seemed the experiences, approaches and techniques that worked so well for me over the years cried out to be shared, and now preserved, for all those who share the passion of empowering frightened children in a medical setting.

As you read through the following chapters, remember you don't have to perfect every skill suggested. When you go to an elaborate buffet, chances are you don't eat everything presented. You probably sample a large variety of foods in small quantities and then go back for more of what appeals to you the most. That very same idea applies to the principles in this book. You don't have to master and perfectly digest each and every chapter. Sufficiently sample the variety, pick what you like and get proficient at just a few of the skills you're most drawn to. That's all you'll need to enjoy being remarkably successful in bringing out the best in children who are in fear.

More than an intellectual understanding, the principles in this book are the result of the motivations of my heart. The way of the heart is the strongest suit I most naturally possess. It was inherited. My mother gave to me.

Watching my mother relate to our family on her narrowly escaped deathbed in the hospital after a potentially fatal heart attack, gave me a sudden and unexpected realization. Here lies a person who possesses everything she could ever possibly need to face death with astounding dignity. Her unique expression of love and compassion is what made that possible. She was a school crossing guard by trade and demonstrated more intelligence where it really mattered in life than one might come to expect. I am blessed to be her son and honored to share the DNA in her heart.

What you will find in the following pages will not include impressive, clever phrases or catchy, articulate linguistics. What you will find is a 110 percent effort to share with you, as simply and directly as I can, how necessary heart medicine is in your work. Don't believe that by merely thinking about your heart that you're acting from there. I challenge and invite you to steep yourself in that which opens the depths of your heart and stay there until you are finished reading this book. My purpose is to teach you how you too can have a profound impact on children's lives by simply understanding the language they speak. There is no degree you could possibly earn in any university that would bring you closer to that language. Open your heart here, as widely as you would open your mind in the most prestigious school of learning.

What Is Your Deepest Fear?

"Our deepest fear is not that we are inadequate. Our deepest fear is that we are powerful beyond measure. It is our light not our darkness that most frightens us. . . .

Your playing small does not serve the world. There is nothing enlightened about shrinking so that other people won't feel insecure around you. . . . We are all meant to shine as children do. . . . It's not just in some of us, it's in everyone. And as we let our own light shine, we unconsciously give other people permission to do the same. As we are liberated from our own fear, our presence automatically liberates others."

Marianne Williamson from *A Return To Love*

1: Start with Yourself

A *frequently asked question I have heard over the years in* working successfully with reducing or eliminating fear in children in a medical setting has been — where do I begin? If I were to create a quick-start guide, my answer would be this: the place to start is always with you. It's important that your very first step is taken in the right direction, so all that follows is on the right path.

Take an honest, objective look at your own inner state in relation to how you currently work with young frightened children. What is your comfort level or immediate reaction when faced with the challenge? How would you describe your overall expression of yourself when placed in that situation? Take a moment to examine that in detail. Understanding your own responses is the key to initiating successful interactions with kids in fear because you're going to take the lead, set the pace, and influence the outcome by your very attitude and presence. In order to have successful interactions, you need to be clear on your own tendencies and how you manage them.

Your Own Response to the Child's Fear

How you respond to the fear dramatically impacts the direction it's going to take. The most common example is when a child falls down in front of a parent. The parent's reaction teaches the child how to react themselves. An overreaction by the parent teaches the child that in this situation, you panic just like mom and you cry because you're supposed to. Your mom is expecting it! A calm or objective response leaves a lot more possibilities for the child to consider, including getting up by themselves and continuing to play, even if it hurts a little.

Every child you see in fear of experiencing a medical intervention is looking to you to know how to respond — whether you think it seems like it or not. By not responding in fear, your demeanor invites the child to consider other possibilities. You must develop a sensitive awareness of your internal and external reactions and responses because you're going to influence your patients extensively.

I was once asked by hospital administration to be present during a meeting with several family members who had recently experienced the death of their son. They didn't ask me to say anything and, in fact, preferred that I didn't. "We want you there because you have a calming presence," they said, illustrating the point that how one presents oneself can greatly influence a situation.

The Mirror Technique

The next time you go into a child's hospital room, pretend you are holding up a mirror directly in front of yourself. What do you see? Remember that how you interpret the situation the child is in will be written all over your face. It will affect what you say, how you say it and all of your nonverbal language as well. All that you're thinking and feeling internally manifests as an external expression and in turn will have an impact on the child. If you are uncomfortable, children may not know how to read your nervous energy. They may misinterpret it, not know how to respond to it, or mistake your nervousness for their own. It's so important for you to realize how frequently young children internalize events. Oftentimes, they believe they are responsible for things that happen out of pure innocence.

I remember when my four-year-old daughter, Nicole, took a little too much time getting into the car as we were going somewhere in a hurry. I had asked her to hurry up while she was full of distractions typical for her age. When we finally got buckled in and I turned the ignition, the car wouldn't start.

Immediately, my daughter took a short breath, turned to me and said, "Daddy, did I do that?" Because she took too much time getting into the car she believed she was responsible for it not starting. Children will internalize circumstances and events and blame themselves without your even knowing about it or being aware that the process is happening. A more typical example is when children feel responsible for their parents' divorce. If you stand before a child uncomfortable yourself or with any kind of fear, it's not unreasonable for a child to believe on a subconscious level that he or she is somehow the cause of it. I'm not suggesting that you have to walk on eggshells with the kids, but awareness of these subtleties helps you to stay focused on the child, which makes a big difference in how well you connect with each other.

For all these reasons, how you present yourself, respond to children's medical conditions and react to their fear is critical. Become acutely aware of the primary verbal and nonverbal message you deliver from the very beginning. Fine-tune that message into one of confidence and certainty of a positive inter-action, and you have taken your first step in the right direction.

The vast majority of successful interactions take place within you first, even before stepping into the room or meeting the child. When you are grounded and comfortable within yourself, your energy is conserved, not wasted. You're not dealing with your own thoughts, feelings and attitudes at the same time you're helping the kids with theirs. Your energy is focused, and you become more available to the child on many different levels. You listen better, think smarter and are more likely to make better professional judgments. The weight of your own uncertainty that would have become a solid and tangible barrier is removed. Now, you can allow the presence of the child to penetrate your being. You become more receptive to their perspective. When you get out of your own way by eliminating self-created barriers, you can become immersed in how the child sees the situation, and then all your action emerges spontaneously from that standpoint. The active approach to take with each individual child becomes more apparent to you.

I once worked with a fourteen-year-old boy who exhibited excessive fear over having to inject himself with insulin. He was diagnosed with diabetes, and I was there to educate him and his family. He became very evasive, used delay tactics, and literally got up to leave the room in tears when it came time to take

19

his shot. I remained unaffected by his behavior and just observed him without judgment. I didn't force the issue, or insist he act like a man, I just absorbed and observed his phobic behavior.

The next day, it just so happened, a girl his age was newly diagnosed on the floor in a room right next to him. Seeing the perspective of this boy so clearly, the action for me to take seemed to present itself on its own. Middle adolescents (aged 13–15 years) are highly susceptible to peer pressure. I put the two teenage kids together in the same room and taught the self-injection skills to the girl first, who without hesitation, injected herself dauntlessly. The boy knew what he had to do now. He had to get over it! He stood up nervously and quickly walked back to his room as I followed behind. He took the syringe from my hand and directly faced the intensity of his own phobia. Sitting on the edge of his bed, he slowly then deliberately injected himself with a moan. To his own surprise, he discovered his phobia hurt more than the needle itself! Over the next few years, this boy went on to become a mentor for children at Camp Coqui, a camp for kids with diabetes.

When you look at a reluctant child who is about to undergo a medical intervention, you begin to develop a sense as to how you can creatively help them. Enter that space receptive, passive and willing to learn. It's almost like you're absent, and the only energy present becomes their own. You take in the fear of the child and take over the direction the energy of it is going to take, as you will see in the following chapters. If you're not very familiar or comfortable with this use of the term "energy," then perhaps I can best explain my meaning in the following story.

My four-year-old nephew, Kobe, expresses himself remarkably well for his age. The other day, he visited his other uncle, my brother, Tom.

When it came time to leave, Tom said to Kobe, "I want to hug you good-bye."

"No ... I don't want a hug," Kobe replied.

"Well, I'm going to hug you anyway," Tom said, and knelt down and gave him a big squeeze. Kobe didn't struggle or resist, nor did he reciprocate.

He simply looked at my brother and said, "I'm sorry. I didn't accept your hug!"

Kobe, Age 6

Most kids would have objected or felt defeated when the actual physical embrace took place. But see it from Kobe's perspective. He didn't accept or participate in the energy or the spirit that takes place when two people hug each other. He just wasn't in the mood.

Fear Changes Shape

Don't be fooled by the initial fear that you see coming from the child, no matter how intensely it presents itself. My experience has shown that however forceful the child's initial presentation of fear appears to be, it's not yet the finished product. Realize you are entering into a process, not a single event, and you are witnessing only the beginning phase. I have learned how not to be overly concerned with the child's initial reaction, because I've seen with my own eyes the energy of fear shift, change shape and reframe itself, with help of course. With a little practice and dedication, the child's fear can become a little bit like clay in your hands.

This fear is like a Halloween mask that momentarily takes you back when it's pushed in your face, but then you quickly realize it's only an innocent, mischievous child underneath. Don't mistake the intensity of the fear as the end result. Always remember, what you see is not necessarily what you get. That part is up to you more than you realize, and that's why this first chapter is so important for you to understand.

When a child's fear confronts you, don't be concerned if it hits you with a force and knocks you off balance. How you respond when that happens is the critical turning point within you. Where you go from there, mentally and emotionally, is the key to your success and with the children you work with. This is the precise moment you may begin to doubt yourself. It is at this very critical juncture where I have seen many talented healthcare practitioners get off track from lack of awareness. If you accept the child's fear as very powerful and resign yourself to it, and allow the child's emotions to overtake you, you're lost. The child is now in control and can easily see your fear, as well as their own, and you're both finished. What else can two fears do except rhythmically perpetuate themselves?

Instead, remain focused and be alert to this moment within you. Maintain your composure. Simply remain firm in your intention and in your vision that you can help the child find a positive experience.

This concept of energy is critical for you to understand because the one with the strongest energy will dominate the relationship and the interaction. I don't mean physical or forceful energy, but the energy of understanding the comprehensiveness of the situation, and the ability to see past the immediate and into the bigger overall picture.

This very step that's taken within you is the heart and soul of the work of successfully preparing the foundation to allow that fear the space it needs for transformation. Even when it appears grounded in paralyzing fear from the child's point of view, that's not necessarily where it's going to end up. Through your work together, fear finds a new perspective and with your guidance can be transformed into confidence. That's why I love working with children so much. They are remarkably creative and resourceful in working with fear, and I invite you to be as well. I have experienced countless times with the kids at Camp Coqui who face, overcome and break through their fears when faced with challenges. They climb high walls and poles, balance on a thin wire high in the trees, jump off platforms and go down zip lines. For the first five minutes, they're stuck in I can't, I can't — you work with them, they do it and then delight in their very ability. In my experience, the fear in a medical setting is really no different.

Recognize Your Own Authority

When my sister, Nancy, was five years old, she screamed and cried and insisted that my mother make it stop raining so she could go outside and play. Nancy firmly believed that, as an adult, my mother had the power to control the weather but just didn't want to, so she continued pitching a fit.

Understand the powerful position you are automatically assigned as a healthcare provider. You *can* take control of the situation, and often the perspective of those you work with is that you're expected to. You can literally change the direction the fear may self-preservingly believe it needs to take and

DENNIS SHARES HIS UNDERSTANDING
OF THE CONCEPT OF "ENERGY."

"DID YOU EVER NOTICE THAT MOM'S SMILE STAYS HERE EVEN WHEN SHE'S GONE?"

coax it into cooperation, which is very self-empowering for the child. Don't discount a young child's ability to transform fear, especially when they see how much you believe in them as their caregiver. That degree of confidence, however, must be present within *you* first. Only then will your confidence in the child be real enough to make a difference. Once the child sees the tangible confidence you have in them, it's easier for them to find it within themself. Suddenly, the child uses the energy of their own fear to fuel their imagination, trust and cooperation and face the fear with self-empowering dignity and pride. Dignity sounds like an unusual word to use with a child, but in my experience they are amazingly willing to express it with our help. They're not running around fragmented at the mercy of an overwhelming emotion because together you are initially steering the energy into a relationship of love, trust, and coop-eration — and then into a state of self-empowerment for the both of you.

You're in a position of authority and responsibility to see to it that the child has a favorable experience. Neither you nor the child are the victim here. No victim consciousness allowed! Do not engage yourself in the thought that you are at the mercy of a screaming, terrified child who is out of control as you helplessly stand by unable to do anything about it. Take charge of out-of-control emotions by exhibiting control yourself through your vocal tone, voice, breathing and body language. Show them directly through your example. As the adult, a knee-jerk reaction or worse, complete indifference, is the last thing you want to demonstrate.

For example, I recently heard screaming as a phlebotomist was working with a young five-year-old who needed her blood drawn. The child became afraid as soon as she saw the technician while she was walking back to the treatment room with her mother. The technician made no effort to intervene on the little girl's behalf and just started to draw her blood. The child screamed bloody murder as she was held, and her blood sample was obtained. Her screams were heard throughout the floor, and the look on every face in the waiting room reflected her suffering.

When I asked the technician what happened, his nonchalant response was, "She was afraid before I even started working on her." His attitude was one of indifference, as if the child was to blame because she was already afraid before the blood draw began. I believe the child was able to easily sense his lack of compassion and knew he was more interested in obtaining the sample than in caring for her. The technician just wanted to get it over with and took no responsibility to care for her emotional needs. If you were five years old and faced with that situation how might you respond? I'm sure his interaction with her would have been much different if he had focused his attention on the child, showed her his concern, and then communicated with her about her fear.

Take responsibility for how children are responding to you. It's a hard question to ask yourself — How am I contributing to the children's fear? — and then change the way you present yourself to get a better response.

A controlled, deliberate belief that stands firm in knowing empowerment can happen even in the most unlikely circumstances, sends a powerful message. You're not giving up, rolling over and playing dead because you're a helpless victim in the same way the child thinks he or she is. You have much more to offer than that.

Children are much more capable of facing their fears than adults are, and we have much to learn from them in this regard. They are the real teachers, and I view this as the spiritual blessing that's bestowed upon us in doing this work. To me, working with children immobilized by fear *is* spiritual by its very nature. You're being given an opportunity to make a tremendous impact on a child in an emotionally critical moment. Not only can you prevent the proverbial "white-coat syndrome" from developing by unnecessarily traumatizing a frightened child, you can actually teach them how to favorably respond to their own fear in the future.

There is no better feeling than diffusing a burning fear and turning it into an anticlimactic fizzle. In such cases, you and the child will experience a unifying bond and a powerful, lasting memory. The spirit of the interaction stays with both of you for years to come and can be drawn upon as a future template for success. It gets even more exciting when a string of successful interactions begins to occur, and you build momentum from one child to the next. Your confidence soars, and you have moments of standing in the light of the magic of the work as success begins to follow you.

Remember, children are naturally intuitive and will often mirror your affect. Just relax and realize that most often they are really only as scared as you are. Sayings like "Copycat, copycat" and "Monkey see, monkey do" come out of this basic understanding — an understanding that comes from the child's perspective, of course.

So present yourself in the manner you want children to mimic. What is the message you're delivering through physical means such as your body posture and your facial expressions? Emotionally, if your heart could talk, what message would it convey? How receptive are you intellectually and what is your intention? Are you presenting a suitable model for the child to imitate? Once you see these things clearly, you have the opportunity to fine-tune and raise the energy of your own presence. You are now prepared for entry. In a mirror-like fashion, you exhibit the very energy you would like to create in those you treat.

SUMMARY

1) The key to having cooperative interactions with children in fear begins with you. The attitude you display and your own personal response to the child's fear have a direct impact on the child's view of the options available to them. Entering their space with a warm, receptive heart, energetically prepared to protect the child from their own fear, has a dramatic effect on the direction the fear itself will take.

2) Deal with your doubts and fears first so you don't bring that energy into the interaction with the child.

3) How *determined* you are in seeing to it that the child has a positive experience is far more important than how *frightened* the child is. The majority of successful interactions you will experience will have taken place within yourself first.

4) Own your own power and authority as a professional. Young children, especially, believe in your ability as an adult to make good things happen.

5) Children are looking to you to decide where to take their emotions and how to express them.

If you were to see a mirror image of yourself the minute you step into the room of a child, what would you see? Fine-tune your initial presentation to be one of comfort and confidence in the presence of frightened children. *Be* just exactly as you would like them to be. Give them the opportunity to mimic your comfort.

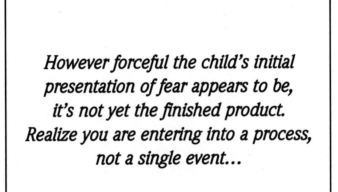

*However forceful the child's initial
presentation of fear appears to be,
it's not yet the finished product.
Realize you are entering into a process,
not a single event...*

*With a little practice and dedication,
the child's fear can become a little
bit like clay in your hands.*

"Imagination is more powerful than knowledge."
–Albert Einstein

2: Apply the Law of Expectations

*W*hat the mind believes tends to be realized. This is one of the most foundational laws taught by hypnotherapists in relation to the power of suggestion. Simply stated, we act on what we believe to be true and make it a realization in our lives. Creating new and favorable expectations and redirecting them in a positive direction is fun. So is watching people act from them.

My favorite example of this basic law is in a personal story I call "I Can't Drive in the Snow." My wife and I were building our house in Asheville, North Carolina, in 1993. During the building process, I subcontracted a man named Mark to hang our dry wall. He usually worked alone, so the job extended into the winter months. One cold December morning he showed up early and promptly went to work. Within a few hours it started to snow. I observed him going to the window, watching the snow and then going back to work. Our home is on top of a knoll surrounded by open hilly pasture, encircled by mountains, now with a magnificent snow-fallen view, which is what I thought he was admiring. I could hear the sound of sawing and pounding as he nailed up the dry wall. It began to snow a little harder when I heard the pounding stop. I went to check on him and he was standing by the window once again with a concerned look on his face.

"I can't drive in the snow," was all he said as he went back to work. The snow continued to fall, and Mark stopped working again. This time he said, "I need to leave because I can't drive in the snow."

A very light blanket covered the driveway, but having grown up in Buffalo I was completely undaunted by it.

"It's not that bad out at all, and I would really like to finish up today if we can," I said.

Reluctantly, he went back to work. Shortly afterward I heard the clamor of tools. As I entered the room, I watched him throw all his tools into a bag with an air of intensity.

He kept repeating, "I need to leave now because I can't drive in the snow." Now in a fury, he packed his things and raced down the front stairs. Puzzled, I followed him outside. In one quick motion, he threw his bag onto the bed of his pick-up, climbed into the cab and turned the ignition. Frantically, he drove down the sloping driveway so fast he missed the turn, continued right across my neighbor's lawn, up an embankment and straight into a telephone pole.

He jumped out of his truck and yelled to me, "Do you see? I told you I can't drive in the snow!"

I had to chuckle inside, thinking to myself, You can't think in the snow, either.

Mark was right. He successfully created his own self-fulfilling prophecy. In fact, he went out of his way to make his belief self-realized. I still don't know how he managed to find that pole, the only obstacle available, just to drive his point across (no pun intended).

When I shared this story with Jeff, a friend of mine, his response was, "That's just an obvious example. In how many ways do we do that in our lives that are so much more subtle?"

I have found that almost everyone I have come in contact with in a hospital setting has their mind made up to some degree on what they expect from a medical interaction. This is true even when the scenario is unfamiliar to them or they have no experience with the situation at hand. The mind finds comfort in clinging to something to call its own. Even unpleasant expectations are better than no expectations at all, because the fear of the unknown is far worse. That unknown can be an unhealthy playground for an over-active imagination. It is here that we as healthcare providers can have the most impact, first by becoming aware of what those expectations are, and then redirecting them into more positive possibilities.

Expectations Determine Outcomes

Jason was an eight-year-old boy with blond hair and blue eyes who sustained a second-degree, four-inch laceration to his forearm after falling off his bike. He was extremely upset about coming anywhere near the emergency room. Crying and visibly frightened, he backed away from the triage nurse, unwilling to even show her his injury.

Jason was afraid of his bleeding, but even more terrified of having to see us, and the prospect of what needed to be done for him. Nancy, at triage, took down the information and assigned him to my room. She handed me his chart and said, "Get the papoose board, you're gonna need it!"

A papoose board is a black, hard wooden board with Velcro straps from top to bottom. The patient is strapped in, outmuscled, and outnumbered. At one time, we rolled up uncooperative patients in a sheet to restrain movement so medical treatment could be accomplished, but this little device works better. Although it sounds appalling, sometimes there is no alternative and it has to be used, even through ear-piercing screams and physical objections. Nurses skilled in preventing its use are not always available, and busy emergency rooms don't always have the luxury of waiting for a child to be ready. Besides, most of us know that left up to the child, they will most likely *never* be ready.

The longer you wait, the more time the patient spends sitting in fear. That's where good nursing skills come into play. Besides knowledge and skill, our job requires a degree of sensitivity and creativity to match the needs of both patient and physician effectively and yes, unfortunately, in a timely manner as well. Even as an emergency room nurse, I took it as a personal challenge to find better ways than to use a child-restraining device.

I was able to bring Jason and one of his parents back to the treatment room. I felt as if getting to Jason from the start gave me a distinct advantage. I immediately started setting up expectations and indications as to the direction in which I wanted his experience to unfold. Jason obviously had time to think about all the possible worst-case scenarios on his way to the hospital and in the waiting room. Negative images and feelings were running through his mind and body, reinforcing themselves the longer he waited.

Knowing through experience how easily the mind can be redirected, with confident eye contact and an almost disinterested yawn, I looked at his wound, then at him and said, "Oh, is that all? I can show you a real easy way to fix this." He didn't say anything as he hesitantly followed behind me with his mom. I kept repeating that I knew an easy way for us to work on his arm.

Finally, after hearing me repeat myself so many times, he abruptly stopped dead in his tracks at the entrance to the treatment room, looked directly into my eyes and said, "An easy way to fix this?" His questioning tone of voice was almost demanding, as if to say, What are you talking about, these things can't possibly be easy! Right there I knew I had him! Those few seconds were the entire turning point.

Learn to recognize where, within your interaction, lies the primary opportunity to create a major shift in expectations. Concentrated moments like this come suddenly. You have to be very alert to recognize and respond to them. Key moments include when a child questions you, repeats your positive words or phrases, or appears confused.

Confusion is a tremendously powerful tool to use when working with the mind. Practice putting the mind in shock. Deliberately confuse it. For a split second the mind stops whirling in its worn out, repetitious groove. That's your window of opportunity. Give it a new "loop" to follow because that's what it feeds off of in this situation, patterns and repetition. So much energy has been going into negative thinking that it's ready for an "out." It's ripe for change because it's tired. Then all the energy that has been going into fear and distrust (which moves into the body as tension) is suddenly released! Think of all the tremendous momentum of energy you have here at your disposal.

Fear is energy in motion. One of the most important things to realize is that fear can be used as a valuable jumping board. It does not necessarily have to move against you or your patient. Although the word "fear" connotes negativity, the energy and momentum generated by this emotion can be used to produce a positive outcome. If you had this force of energy available to you and your patient, how would you use it? For me, I shoveled every last ounce into Jason's now fertile imagination.

"Let me show you how. Lie down here," I said, with a tone of absolute certainty, determined to make his experience a good one. Deliberately breaking eye contact so as not to create a challenge, I turned away from him while motioning to the stretcher. Under his own power and free will, he got up on the stretcher and sat there for a moment, before agreeing to lie down and go through an imaginary scenario of what he needed to do when the doctor came in. I knew the papoose board was history. His mom sat silently in the corner observing our interactions.

"If you just do two simple things it will be so easy," I said, his eyes glued to mine. Our faces were close together and we were at eye level.

"Make your arm like it's sound asleep, just like this," I said, picking up my own arm and plopping it down like a dead weight on the gurney right next to him.

"Pick up my arm," I asked. He lifted up my heavy, lifeless arm a couple inches and dropped it with a thud. He tried to smile as he saw how relaxed I had made it.

"Now, you try," I said. Eagerly, he took all the tension out of his wounded arm as I lifted it up a few inches and let it softly plop down.

"It's as easy as that," I repeated. His eyes reflected an intensity consistent with his prior fear while they still remained fixed to mine. Deliberately removing tension from the rest of his body followed.

"What is your favorite thing to do? Do you have a favorite sport or activity that you love to play?" I asked.

"Playing basketball with my friends," Jason said.

"Okay, let's play," I said. "The second thing I want you to do is close your eyes and imagine you're playing basketball right now."

The boy closed his eyes and went through a practice run of imagining playing basketball, describing a few things to me about what that was like for him.

"That's all you have to do, and you won't even know the doctor is working on you," I said. I completely avoided words contrary to the expectation I was trying to create.

Your words should be consistently reinforcing the big picture of how the *total experience* is going to end up. Remember, we are giving the mind a new

35

loop. Keep repeating words or phrases your patient can lock onto. Tell those key words or phrases to the doctor and everyone else working with the child so they can reinforce them as well. For Jason, those words were "comfortable" and "easy" rather than telling him there would be "no pain." Jason also realized that we were going to go through this together. He knew I wasn't going anywhere and that I would be by his side to nurse him through it. We had trust. We had rapport.

Dr. Neimis entered the room as I was preparing the sterile instrumentation he would need. Jason and I repeated our steps. His eyes closed, his arm went to "sleep" and we started playing basketball together. He described what he "saw" as he started to play. The doctor cleaned his wound with Betadine. We kept on playing.

"Who are you playing with?" I asked.

"My best friend who lives next door," he said.

"Tell me how you are dressed," I asked, just before the doctor was about to inject his wound to make it numb. It is very important to encourage the imagination to be *highly detailed,* at the point where the most discomfort (notice I didn't say pain) may be felt. Jason used exceptional detail as he described the type and color of his brand of sneakers, and even mentioned something about the laces as the needle pierced his wound several times surrounding it with 1% Xylocaine. Jason's detailed imagination was so powerfully engaged he never moved.

"What clothes are you wearing?" I asked, to ground him further into his imagination.

"My white T-shirt and a blue pair of shorts," he responded, as more detail was encouraged and exchanged. The doctor curiously glanced at Jason as he continued injecting.

"Are you playing by yourself?" I asked.

"Oh no, I'm playing with my friend who lives next door," he said.

"Are you at his house?" I questioned.

"No, we are playing at mine because there are no cars in my driveway right now," he said.

At this point Jason's arm was anesthetized, and I knew the hardest part was over. We continued in our imagery for about twenty minutes until the doctor and his assistant injected, cleaned, debrided and sutured the wound. We were so absorbed in our own conversation together, little was said to the doctor until he finally got into the basketball conversation himself. Working as a team, reinforcing the same idea among all the caregivers, this child was actually told what kind of experience he could expect to have and followed it through to completion. He was literally talked into it, despite his earlier perceived version of what happens in a place like this!

Doctor Neimis removed the instruments and the sterile drape, telling Jason, "You can get up now."

"We're all done?" he squealed, as he sat up, beaming with a smile for the very first time. He hopped off the stretcher with a pride I'm sure he will carry most of his life. He was full of surprise and delight, infused with a dignity and poise he had given to his eight-year-old spirit. No white-coat syndrome was created here today. But the best was yet to come!

"What was the experience like for you?" I asked with anticipation. He said, and I will never forget his words, "It was like a bumble bee was buzzing around my arm and he dropped his stinger, but it bounced off!"

I put my arm around his proud small shoulders as together we walked toward his mom, who was grinning from ear to ear after what she had witnessed.

Ask Patients to Share Their Experience in Their Own Words

Always ask your patients to share their experience of what it was like for them, once the procedure has ended. The creativity of their quotes will delight and amaze you as you add them to your own bank of positive experiences. Asking also reminds you that it was their work just as much as yours, and you did it as a team.

Beware of your own ego. That can be an occupational hazard when you get on a roll. We are but guides, sharing a skill and a passion. The love and energy we give comes back to us tenfold. Receive your gratis in this way. Don't allow your ego to diminish it by getting yourself all puffed out.

Start a collection of those precious quotes like Jason's, and carry them all with you to your next encounter. Among all the children I imagine in my mind's eye walking with me and behind me when I enter a new patient's room, who have faced and conquered their fears, I see Jason at the front of that crowd.

Just stepping into a hospital environment, children are already engaged in the powerful law of expectations. In fact, it's set into motion before they even get there. Once they enter the hospital, in their own way children become entranced by the physical surroundings, the smells, the uniforms, and the intimidation that exists in relinquishing some degree of control the very environment is known for. Couple these circumstances with the child's natural ability for vivid imagination, and the law is in full effect.

To discover imagination, a teacher placed a dot on a blackboard in a schoolroom. When adults were asked what it was, they said, " It's a dot on a blackboard." When children were asked the same question the responses were completely different.

"A small universe," said one child. "A small hole in the blackboard," said another, but my favorite was, "A telephone pole." When encouraged to explain, the child said, "Yes, a telephone pole, but you have to look at it from the top down!" Children can out-imagine adults any time, any place, anywhere.

Recognize the Strength in Your Authority

Working in medicine and nursing makes you privileged in that you are viewed as an authority. Authority figures know how things are done and what we can expect in certain situations. We do this work daily and are experts in knowing how it's done and how people typically respond. We know this based on experience. We also have the reputation and responsibility to correct misconceptions people have and re-educate them on certain medical facts. In short, we change beliefs and we do it for a living on a daily basis.

Couple this perception with a young person's natural propensity for imagination, and you have a simple approach that works.

For example, I recall a young man sitting on a stretcher in the ER saying to me, "Shots hurt."

"Not with the new syringes they make now," I convincingly replied, (notice I didn't say needles). "These are new," as I handed him one to hold, "and you wouldn't know the difference between someone poking you with a finger (as I poked his arm) or giving you a shot. In fact," I repeated, "if your eyes were closed, you wouldn't know which side was the shot and which side was the finger!" How I love to watch the gears of expectation turn by the look on their face. Having said this so many times over the years, I'm completely convinced of it myself. My belief becomes their belief and they willingly choose that very experience. In addition, relaxing the arm like it's asleep is usually all it takes to show them how to receive a shot the next time, in the same relaxed way they would experience having their blood pressure checked. That's exactly what happened as this young man accepted my challenge, closed his eyes and tried to guess on which side I poked my finger, and which side was intramuscularly injected. He paused a moment after opening his eyes, and guessed correctly (lucky guess) but then agreed shots don't have to hurt.

Applying the basic law of expectations has been the focus of my career. To this day it continues to produce success after success. Don't underestimate this simple principle. Realize all of the factors that come into play that favorably set up your ability to change the child's way of thinking. You have the home-court advantage in a medical environment because as a nurse or healthcare professional, you are viewed as an authority figure. You wear a distinct uniform. You are licensed, experienced and respected. You're perceived as caring, loving and nurturing. You're seen as a friend, a patient advocate, and an educator. Combine these attributes with your own personal touch and abilities and you have so many reasons for success.

For all our patients, fear and apprehension take tremendous energy to maintain; and if there is a way out of it, patients are ripe for considering an alternative. Most children are at least willing to try to have a pleasant experience and will cooperate just enough to get it. Between these factors lies the opportunity to create favorable changes in thinking patterns as opposed to what patients might expect to happen. Changing a negative mental loop to a more positive one is an important first step. But don't stop there. We must also provide the tools and show patients how to continue moving forward after that first step is taken, while supporting their newfound confidence. Some of these tools include breath work, simple distraction, eye closure, and detailed mental imagery.

I remember sharing this premise with Dr. Wilson from the ER. He didn't agree.

"I tried giving this type of positive suggestion to a patient," he said. "I told him injecting the wound to make it numb wouldn't hurt. I then injected the wound and the patient howled, 'It hurts! It hurts!' My patients might lose confidence in me so I don't want to feel like I'm lying to them. Their trust in me is too valuable to risk," he said.

"Did you do anything else besides tell him it wouldn't hurt?" I asked.

"No," he responded.

"Did you give the patient a method to use, like focusing on slow, deep abdominal breaths, or ask him to close his eyes and take himself mentally elsewhere?" I questioned.

"No, I really didn't do any of that," he said. It was then that he realized a second step was needed.

Two distinct factors come into play. You must set an expectation *and* give the patient tools to work with to support those expectations in your presence. It helps to keep them on track. No healthcare professional wants to feel as if his or her reputation or trust is sacrificed or, worse, that the patient feels they have been lied to. You have to work them through the process, acting as an anchor of support to keep them headed in the right direction.

That's why nurses are so valuable. Easing a patient's emotional discomfort is just as important as easing their physical discomfort. Don't view them as being separate from each other. Because they are so intertwined, you must address them as one. Dr. Wilson could not easily do his work, debride the patient's wound and observe for subtle changes all at the same time. A team approach always works best whenever possible. Once you have set the expectation with the patient, be alert, and watch for subtle changes in breathing, movement, a frown, or other unfavorable facial changes. As soon as you see these cues, deepen your method. For instance, you might choose breath work to take tension out of the body. Have the patient breathe all the way down to their belly, or breathe a slow, prolonged exhale right along with them in order to help them refocus and establish a rhythm. Ground them again into the mental images of what they are seeing in their mind, encouraging and asking for specific detail. Detail in mental imagery is absolutely mandatory.

A story from the early 1900s that has been relayed from student to student over the years demonstrates this important point. A Zen martial arts master went to his doctor. He had an obtrusive tumor-like growth in a nasal cavity obstructing his breathing. The master sat on the doctor's table (accompanied by several students) closed his eyes, slowed his breathing and physically slouched in posture (releasing tension) while taking his mind elsewhere. The doctor inserted a knife and bit by bit removed the tumor without so much as a flinch from the master. It was a lengthy, bloody procedure. When it was done, his students immediately understood the meaning of the word "master," as mastery over one's self.

Teaching children to remain in control of their responses even for moments or the time it takes to do a procedure is teaching the valuable life skill of self-mastery. It's a powerful, positive experience they will remember and refer to for the rest of their life.

In fact, guiding children to their own source of strength is part of the tremendous pay-off we get in this profession. These children will never forget you and the positive impact you have made at a vulnerable time in their lives. Can you not recall simple, seemingly innocuous interactions with key people in your own life that meant so much to you that they are etched in your mind forever? What a benefit of the profession! However small the act may seem, you get to impact people's lives and participate in creating a loving, life-long memory.

People Never Forget You When You Empower Them

A dialysis patient I once worked with, named Manny, called out my name as I walked down a medical clinic corridor. We hadn't seen each other for over eight years. He was so excited to see me that he was beaming.

41

The first thing he said to me was, "You changed history for me," in regard to how deep intramuscular injections could be painlessly taken. That was his eight-year association with me. Just seeing me still brought up the expectation that deep injections don't have to hurt! He would always remember me as someone who gave him the tools to "show up for himself" in a way that empowered him. Fear was replaced with empowerment, which was operating at peak efficiency eight years later. Few professions touch lives so persistently.

The parents of children approach me quite often years after an interaction to stop and thank me for the simplest things. I believe the power of intention and the commitment to making a difference needs only one person — you! How we impact the lives of children, transforming their view of themselves beyond childhood and into their adulthood, may not always be known.

Young adults choosing medicine or nursing as a profession may very well be due to an earlier childhood experience they had with a physician, nurse or other medical professional.

One Saturday morning when my wife, Lydia, was a child, she was watching cartoons. The TV screen was blurry, and she tried to fix it by lifting the corner of the television set up, as it was pinching the power cord. She lifted it too far up and it fell from the stand. The corner end landed on the top of her left foot and split it wide open. She remembers looking at how deep her wound was, as she ran yelling and screaming to get her dad. Wrapping the bleeding foot in a T-shirt and tying a knot, her dad called his wife at work and together they went to the hospital. Lydia recalls the bleeding and throbbing pain while waiting at red light after red light wondering to herself — Are we ever going to get there? The hospital took her in immediately and proceeded to work.

She vividly recalls the doctor holding onto her foot too tightly as the nurses around her chanted, "Don't move, don't move." At this point, Lydia was thinking to herself, He doesn't have to hold onto my foot so hard, I'm not going to move it. Apparently, no one checked in with Lydia to see how she was doing. The ER staff expected a lack of cooperation on her part. Lydia's expectations at this point were quite the opposite. She viewed the hospital as a place that could help her, and she was glad to be there. In her mind's eye, she was glad to cooperate and willing to do what was asked of her.

Recalling the story, she remembers the nursing staff's only instructions, "Don't move" and "Don't look." Apparently, she was fascinated with the whole affair and wanted to watch them irrigate, clean and prepare the wound for suturing. Due to the misconception that Lydia would become fearful and move, the head of her stretcher was lowered so she couldn't watch anymore.

"Oh darn," she said to herself. When it was over, the team was surprised that she never cried and never moved her foot.

When asked by the medical staff how she was able to do that, her response was, "It wasn't my foot." She pretended it was somebody else's foot! She was watching just like everybody else. A room full of people working on a foot, but the foot didn't belong to anybody in the room. How's that for childhood imagination!

The funny thing was, nobody told her to do anything. She came up with the whole idea on her own. Lydia expected their help on the way to the hospital knowing within herself, she was going to a place where people knew how to fix things like this. When Lydia was told not to move she recalls asking herself, How am I going to do that? "That's when the idea came to me," she said. She was seven years old at the time.

Today, as a nurse practitioner, Lydia knows that even though the nursing staff had negative expectations of their own and were disconnected from her fascination with the whole affair, her own expectations prevailed.

"They were very kind to me," she recalls. That kindness coupled with her intrinsic fascination in medicine is what led her into the nursing profession.

Experience has taught me that children's imaginations are profoundly engaged without the slightest bit of awareness on our part. Yet this constitutes the peak of our possibilities as nurses — to mold and nurture that imagination into an experience our patients will always remember. It's not hard to discover what expectations are going on inside their heads. Most children will tell you if you just ask. Any probing question will uncover what beliefs are in place.

If you're not sure, ask, "What are you thinking about with your injury? Do you know how we fix this?" If they answer, "I don't know," then you are open to set the expectations creatively according to the situation. If they are unpleasant, redirect them. You can help them understand the natural progression of things like x-rays, wound cleaning, etc., and how they will experience all that needs to be done with you helping them through it.

Help children choose the frame of mind they want as they go through the process, regardless of how the process unfolds. For example, one child engaged his imagination into believing he was a cartoon superhero who had unusual super-powers emanating from his right leg. With help, he remained in focused imagination while lying on the stretcher for longer than necessary due to minor bedside surgical complications.

Occasionally you'll uncover a bad experience the child's brother or sister had, and they are anticipating the same. Rarely are children so mentally fixed on anticipating the worst that they don't want to part with their own frightening ideas, even when it might look that way. In my experience, in spite of appearances, children *want* to reconsider their expectations and invite a better experience for themselves. Adults tend to be more rigid in this regard, perhaps because as adults egos are more at stake. Whatever the reason, adults usually need more time to be persuaded than children do.

I was preparing a fifty-six-year-old woman for surgery. She kept telling me how tense, uptight and afraid she was, and that she was certain her experience was going to be miserable and uncomfortable.

"I can help you with that," I offered.

"Oh no, honey," she replied. "I'm always like this and felt the same way before my last surgery," she insisted.

"But," I said, "I hate to see you put under anesthesia thinking and feeling the way you are right now. Here, let me help you." I took a slight step toward her.

"Oh, no, honey," she repeated as she continued to lament.

Then her family came in and gathered around her bed. As her dramatic performance unfolded, her family huddled closer to her, placing their hands on her and lavishing her with looks of attention and confirmation of her plight. No one was going to break through that, and I was no exception. The secondary gains of the behavior were huge. Her actions and beliefs were a direct pay-off to receiving an overabundance of love, affection and attention before she was carted off. She knew exactly what she was doing. Children are not so complex. Although surprisingly clever, they aren't quite as calculating as adults and usually prefer to keep things simple and to the point.

"Papaw, I want some beeow [beer]," my four-year-old daughter Nicole tells her grandfather. He's watching her for us today and is sipping on a bottle of beer.

"I can't do that," he says. "Your father would kill me."

"If you don't, I'll tell him you did anyway!" Nicole replies.

In relaying this story to me, I recall my father-in-law saying, "Darn! Outwitted by a four-year-old." Children like to get straight to the point.

Find Your Confidence

Medical professionals new to the idea of creating positive expectations may find it easier to start small and then graduate to those ideas that are a bit of a stretch. In this way, you start growing outside your comfort zone. In a very short time, you end up abandoning your perceived limitations until you get to the point that you're amazed by the ability and the imagination you share with kids. Don't doubt yourself. Remain confident throughout the wide range of results you'll experience, especially in the beginning.

I can think of no man who better exemplifies self-confidence than John Dennis. Since the age of eight, he had a dream to sail around the world alone in a small boat. Only fifty people have ever accomplished that. While not a professional sailor himself, members of his family were. Then he developed adult onset diabetes, and for a while his expectations of himself and his abilities changed. Now, not only was he not a professional sailor and lacked funding for his dream, he had a chronic disease to deal with. No one with diabetes had even tried before, because of the physical demands and potential risks of low blood sugar while alone on the seas. Yet, John couldn't accept the thought of a dream lost forever. He worked hard to get his blood sugar under control. He refused to see his medical condition as a disqualification to participate in that dream and stood firm once again in his expectations of himself and his abilities.

Eight hundred and fifty-four corporations said no to his request for sponsorship. The eight hundred and fifty-fifth said yes, enabling John to live his dream and embark on his journey. Talk about patience, confidence and tenacity!

Our mental outlook determines so much of what we experience in our personal and professional lives. "As a man thinketh within his heart, so is he." (Proverbs 23:7)

SUMMARY

1) Most children already have their minds made up to some degree as to what it is they expect to happen when they come to the hospital. Fear often accompanies them, and it is not unusual for this fear to be unreasonably magnified depending on the individual, the situation and the degree of injury. Use your initial approach, your very first intervention with them, as a primary opportunity to start the process of setting new expectations as to how their procedure will be experienced.

2) Literally, talk children into their experience, reinforcing a positive expectation throughout your interaction with them.

3) Use keywords or phrases like "I can show you how *comfortably* this can be done," or "This can be done so *easily*," and repeat those words frequently.

4) When you're working with children, learn to recognize where your opportunities lie in order to shift their expectations or to continue reinforcing the positive expectations you already started. Examples of key moments include:

   a. when a child questions you as to why you keep saying their procedure can be done comfortably or that you know an easy way to do it. It's as if you know a secret and they have become curious about it;

   b. when a child repeats your reassuring words that their experience can be a positive one;

   c. when there is an obvious change in facial expression;

   d. when the child suddenly appears confused;

   e. when the child makes their first effort at cooperating with you when previously they would not agree to anything; and

   f. when anything happens that seems significant to you even though it may be subtle.

5) Realize the power and authority carried in your very uniform, your profession and the environment you work in. You are the expert as far as they are concerned and, if necessary, you decide for them how things happen in your environment. I once heard an oral surgeon tell his patient who was

47

afraid of blood that "Bleeding is not part of the procedure" after he extracted a tooth.

6) Consider coming from this perspective: While there are things children cannot control in a selected procedure, they can control (with your help) the frame of mind they choose while going through it.

7) Be a designer, an interior decorator of the mind. Stay confident and have fun.

8) When you have a success, elicit feedback from the child, asking in their own words what the experience was like for them. Collect those valuable quotes as you gain momentum from one child to the next.

9) Develop a tendency to come into a situation by bombarding the patient with positive statements and an enthusiastic energy. Then, take control of how they are going to respond and what you want them to do to get that response. Repeat the same expectation over and over, overwhelming their senses and insisting on their best possible experience. Never give up on wanting it for them. Children will sense that intention and follow it through to completion. Experience fuels you with the power to create.

10) Remember, absolutely anybody can drive in the snow, once they expect they can — even Mark!

Just stepping into a hospital environment, children are already engaged in the powerful law of expectations.

—•—— ⧚✦⧚ ——•—

"The ability to bring out the best in people comes
from a willingness to see the best in people."
—Robert Luka

—•—— ⧚✦⧚ ——•—

3: Use the Power of Intention

*I*ntention is defined as *"an aim that guides all action." It comes from* the Latin root *intendere,* "to stretch toward." To put it simply, intention is the passion and purpose that goes on inside of you that determines the outcome of your interactions in the world around you.

Intention has always come quite naturally to me working in healthcare. One of my earliest experiences of how powerfully your intention speaks was during my first job in a hospital setting as an orderly while in high school. My duties included taking vital signs, preparing patients for surgery, and lifting heavy patients out of bed who had partial paralysis from a stroke. Oh, did I mention flirting with pretty nurses? Taking bodies to the morgue was also one of my duties. That wasn't what I had in mind, but seeing death up close in adults and children as a teenager helped me learn how to place value on the present moment. The majority of my work consisted of moving patients from their hospital bed and taking them to surgery, radiology or special procedures.

While transporting a man on a stretcher one day, we arrived in the nuclear medicine department. He stopped me, looked into my eyes and said, "You know, you can really tell who cares about you in this place and who is just doing a job. I want to thank you." I was surprised by his compliment because our conversation had been so short. Nothing out of the ordinary had transpired between us that wasn't part of my normal routine — and that's exactly my point. Intention is like an internal broadcasting beacon that shouts your internal state of being. It permeates and affects everything you say and do. Your facial expressions or lack thereof, your body posture, the way you carry yourself, the degree and type of eye contact and, most importantly, the message that emanates from behind your eyes. Even the way a person breathes and touches is influenced. The sum total of your energy is expressed on a universally understood level, and these are just the nonverbals! What about your speech, word choice, volume, pace and, most importantly, the tone of your voice?

Intention Comes Naturally

Expressing your intention comes naturally when you're relaxed and settled in the present moment and have passion for what you do. You're happy with where you are and what you're doing and not thinking about the past or some future need. You're simply here and now.

Perhaps the story of Sarah is the best example I can give you of the power and meaning of intention. I met her in Mission Hospital in Asheville, North Carolina. She was five years old and newly diagnosed with type 1 diabetes. Her body stopped producing insulin, making it unable to control her blood sugar. Sarah had all the typical symptoms — increased thirst, getting up to urinate three or more times in the middle of the night, excessive hunger and weight loss. With this type of diabetes, the symptoms and onset are very sudden, leaving little time to adjust to the diagnosis itself and the emotional impact that follows. Sarah and her mom had already met the doctor and were made aware of the treatment plan — multiple daily insulin injections and frequent blood sugar testing. Sarah, of course, was not fully aware of what all this would mean to her at this point.

As the diabetes patient and family educator assigned to hospital patients, I had the opportunity to work with Sarah to teach her and her mom how to draw blood from her finger, to check her blood sugar reading and then take an insulin shot. Mom was very nervous about how her daughter was going to respond to this treatment, realizing this same routine would need to be repeated three to four times a day, every day from now on.

It's funny how the children and I always seem to time it just right to meet each other. At the time, our department only saw about three children a year with this diagnosis. Despite rotating hospital coverage with four other coworkers, the kids and I always managed to find each other. I love everything about working with these children. Children can learn without fear even if fear is part of the present situation, and they are capable of much more than many adults give them credit for. Despite the fact that the nursing staff had warned me she was very obstinate, I was excited about meeting Sarah and looked forward to working with her as I knocked on her door.

"Come in," her mom responded, as Sarah, who was sitting on the side of the bed, slid over closer to her mom as soon as she saw me enter.

"Hi, Sarah," I said, as I looked into her eyes with a big smile. "Gimme five," as I held up my hand for her to slap in an effort to make contact and break the ice. Willingly, with a thin smile, she played along.

"I brought something for you," I said, as I presented her with a box, which had the glucose-testing meter inside. As Sarah investigated the box, I introduced myself to Mom and answered several questions she had about how she would soon be taking care of her daughter at home.

After warming up to both of them by sharing some educational information in a friendly manner, it came time to learn how to check Sarah's blood sugar. We opened the box together, and I began demonstrating how the meter worked and how it would be used. Just as the three of us entered the height of my teaching, Sarah realized blood had to be drawn from *her* finger. She stopped abruptly, looked at me, and got up and ran straight into the bathroom, shoving closed the heavy wooden door behind her with a slam! "Click"…now the door was locked, and her stunned mother anxiously looked back at me. I have always thrived on the unexpected and the spontaneity children are known for, but this was ridiculous! What happened next was even more surprising.

I immediately followed the child to the bathroom. Through the door, with a defeated, playful and sincere tone in my voice, I said, "Oh all right, I'll let you use *my* finger."

Instantly, she unlocked the door and came right back out under her own free will.

Whenever I tell this story, everyone always wants to know what I said in that situation to get Sarah out so quickly. What I have to remind everyone of is that it wasn't just the words that made her respond. It was her natural ability to read my loving intention toward her that brought her out. My deep inner sincerity of wanting her to have a positive experience drawing blood and my love for working with children. I had a spirited conviction in knowing Sarah could and would have a positive experience because I was willing to persist and insist on it being so, not only for her but for all the children I worked with. That delicate, intangible energetic vibration of love that surrounds and permeates us is what we respond to, and that is exactly what Sarah responded to when she unlocked the door and came out as fast as she went in. That heavy wooden door was not a barrier for us at all. She sensed my being there was not about my own personal agenda. Logic and word choice had little to do with what gave her the confidence to come right back out of the bathroom, trust me, face her fear of blood (however small, with kids it doesn't matter, blood is blood) then learn to take shots. The power of my intention and her ability to understand it gave her the courage to draw blood from my finger first, and then to help her with her own. Sarah didn't cry or even object when I taught her mom how to inject her with insulin. The look on Mom's face was worth a thousand pictures! It was the last thing she expected because that level of cooperation had not been present.

My experience with Sarah went right into my bank of experiences that fuel the confidence for future encounters. I know so deeply that fear has the potential to be transformed easily and, so often, that the energy of confidence is among the strongest projections sensed by these children. Sarah read my intentions clearly and copied my confidence. As magically as Sarah and I found our way to each other at this point in her life, we met again nine years later, only this time she was a teenager. When we looked into each other's eyes, we immediately recognized each other and were full of smiles as we laughed over the "bathroom incident."

Bring Your Intention Alive

Imagine all of the children you have successfully worked with to break through their fear and find their state of empowerment standing behind you as you enter the room of a new patient and proceed to work. In your heart of hearts, your every intention is that this new child before you will, at the conclusion of your time together, join forces in spirit with that imagined group, as you grow

Sarah, Age 5

and carry the energy of success from one child to the other. These children are connected. We're all connected. Believe that. The power of a loving intention has the ability to energetically bind us and bring us closer together. The language of heart is so simple, so natural, that every person, every culture and every nation universally feels it.

When you enter the room of a frightened child with this in mind, from this perspective, the power of intention comes alive. It fills the room. You can transform the environment by your presence alone. Kids know how to tune into your intention and the universal frequency of love you reflect. Even through their fear they can see how intensely your heart invites, insists on their ability to shift out of fear and be with you cooperatively in that moment. When you're convinced yourself, your intentions become influential and children can sense your belief in them. Like Luke Skywalker in *Star Wars*, you "feel the force." You create the milieu to "Let the force be with you, in you, and around you."

The determination, confidence and passion you have within yourself will decide what you believe is possible. It will change your thinking. How you talk to yourself in the silence of your own mind is where your strength comes from. When you are relaxed and settled in the power of your own intention, you become a generating source of confidence. You bring your energy to the encounter and set the environment ablaze with it. It just kind of spills out of you through an overflowing abundance and everyone in the room exposed becomes enthused by it. At least be open to the idea of how contagious a loving intention can be and let your own experiences decide how dynamically.

Children Are Keenly Aware of Loving Intentions

Children are particularly sensitive to feeling the simplicity of a loving intention toward them and have a natural intuitive sense for knowing who is fond of them. They can read between the lines with adults remarkably well and frequently use this sense to determine how much, or even if, they want to cooperate with you. Robbie was a perfect example.

We were having lunch in honor of Cindy, our department director, on National Bosses' Day. Everybody brought in food, and we gathered around tables in a big classroom. Doctor Humphrey brought in her two-year-old son, Robbie, for the celebration, and he was unfamiliar with everyone in the room. There were about fifteen of us eating including Robbie, who had just found a chocolate-chip cookie. He walked around all the tables and out of fifteen people he passed by, he stopped and showed his cookie to two people in the room, Mary Beth and myself. Robbie stopped to tell me about how big his cookie was, gibber-jabbered in toddler talk for a moment and then sat down to eat it.

My coworker Elaine, who was sitting next to me, remarked — "Did you see that? That little boy stopped to talk to the two people in our department who love to work with kids the most!" It seems, perhaps, that somehow Robbie knew that.

How you hold what you intend is plainly apparent, especially to an innocent child. Because children are young and inexperienced, they are vulnerable. They haven't learned how to protect themselves yet. The power of your intention appeals to the highest potential of that innocence.

It took me a long time to write about and formalize a planned description of how to work with children in a medical setting. The reason for that was that the most common question everyone kept asking me was, "What do you *do* with children that makes your interactions with them so frequently calm and positive?" I was trying to answer the *do* until I realized the answer didn't reside there. How are you *being* with children was the real focus of that question. I discovered that the real substance of our interactions wasn't in what I was doing, but in how I was being with the kids that made all the difference. That's where our abilities lie. The success that happens in the room with the children is really secondary. It's your way of being that sets the stage. The work is done inside you first, before you ever set foot into the room.

Statements of Intention

Intention says, *I choose to live in a world where frightened children and I enjoy working with each other. Together, we'll find a way to have a positive interaction during this medical intervention. I feel honored to be a part of the process. I see the hidden potential inside each new child I work with. I believe children have the innate ability to free themselves of self-limiting fear and substitute it with empowered cooperation. I have a determined, pinpoint, laser-like focus on making this interaction as pleasant as possible. In this space, I passionately invite your participation.*

It doesn't always matter what each individual child brings to the table as far as ability, resources or experiences. Perceive the interaction as a neutral playing field where all children share equally in the opportunity to participate in a stress-free experience. That doesn't mean that they all will. It simply means you never stop holding that intention for them. Maintain the passionate belief that children can empower themselves when given the opportunity, the framework and a little guidance — even if that empowerment comes in a medical environment, which can be intimidating, and involve pain and fear.

Why do I believe in such a thing? Because this has been my experience time and time again: that all these factors combined — your love, passion and intention, and their fear, doubt and pain — culminate somehow to aid in the child's process of transforming their energy into something far more constructive than fear alone. Especially when you tell them they can. Think of the last time your own heart palpitated with fear. You need more than a logical, rational reason to jump out of it. You need the power of trust, which is nothing more than the inverted twin, the flip side of the same coin called fear. It's the same energy. If you can clearly see this fact, then seeing before your eyes a sudden shift in a child's behavior seems more likely. The energy was already there! You don't have to work to create it, it's already there waiting to be converted, ready to be transformed.

I am reminded of the following passage by Baghwan Shree Rajnesh (Osho) called Atisha's Exercise. Go into it deeply.

Transformation

Now he says: Start being compassionate. And the method is, when you breathe in — listen carefully, it is one of the greatest methods — when you breathe in, think you are breathing in all the miseries of all the people in the world. All the darkness, all the negativity, all the hell that exists anywhere, you are breathing it in. And let it be absorbed in your heart.

When you breathe in, breathe in all the misery and suffering of all the beings of the world, past, present and future. And when you breathe out, breathe out all the joy that you have, all the blissfulness that you have, all the benediction that you have. Breathe out, pour yourself into existence. This is the method of compassion: drink in all the suffering and pour out all the blessings. And you will be surprised if you do it. The moment you take all the sufferings of the world inside you, they are no longer sufferings. The heart immediately transforms the energy. The heart is a transforming force: drink in misery, and it is transformed into blissfulness... Then pour it out.

Once you have learned that your heart can do this magic, this miracle, you would like to do it again and again. Try it. It is one of the most practical methods — simple, and it brings immediate results. Do it today and see.

With experience, you begin to see the conversion of fear to trust as a natural movement. As the facilitator of that movement, you share in the blessing of its transformation as the energy is released from a lower vibrational pattern to a higher one. Through your intention, you actively participate in creating a conducive environment. After all, you and the child are a team. If they could do it themselves, your participation wouldn't be needed. But you *are* needed. Far more than you realize, you are needed to share your heart, share your love and together stand in its power and grace.

Intentional Listening

Remember the definition of intention described earlier as "an aim that guides all action?" Well, intentional listening could be defined in a similar way but I would like to be creative here and describe it as an "aim that guides in-action as well," as in listening with a different purpose.

Listen to the child without thinking about how you interpret what is said, but how they interpret it, the perspective of their mind. Do not allow your focus to spin off into memories and experiences of *your own*. Stay in the experience of the child. Listen to the meaning they are attaching to their words. Sounds simple, doesn't it? Try it in normal conversation, and come from the perspective of the other person during the whole dialogue. See how long it takes before you feel compelled to interject how *you* feel about what is being said instead of staying with how *they* feel about it. Can you listen without thinking about what you are going to say in response? You can't really listen to me and think about what you're going to say next at the same time. Can you refrain from giving advice? Use the Zen approach: be the listening.

Staying in the moment and listening to the other person openly, predominately implies that you agree to omit your own way of dealing with the situation. Momentarily leaving out your own thoughts about the situation is the only way to make room for you to understand their thoughts and emotions. When you listen in this way, you will hear subtle associations the child is making with the current situation or with experiences in the past. Now your understanding deepens.

Rapport develops easily with the one who offers himself as an intentional listener. People love to be heard. You automatically become respected and valued if you do just that. Then, challenges put before you become opportunities to get even more creative with each other. Now your approach begins to carry an entirely different message, an entirely different vision. It changes how others perceive you and ultimately how others respond to you.

Become very aware of your intention and the message it's broadcasting. The children you care for are.

SUMMARY

1) Evaluate the intention you have been holding when working with children. What idea, attitude or premise do you currently identify with, and does it give you the results you're looking for?

2) Observe the effect on yourself and others as you hold different intentions in a variety of situations. What outcome were you responsible for producing?

3) Deliberately create your intentions as you would like to see them unfold.

4) "Feel the Force." Acknowledge the ability to transform your environment through your very presence.

5) Try Atisha's exercise.

6) Imagine that every child that has overcome their fear with your assistance comes with you and stands behind you as you enter the room of a new child who is afraid. Be patient, until eventually the room is so crowded with the spirit of empowered kids the fear gets scared and runs away.

7) Listen with the intention of staying in the perspective of the person speaking. Exclude your own feelings and interpretations and simply listen to theirs.

> *With experience, you begin to see the conversion of fear to trust as a natural movement. As the facilitator of that movement, you share in the blessing of its transformation...Through your intention, you actively participate in creating a conducive environment.*

"The three most important words
for a successful relationship are
communication, communication,
and communication."
–Anonymous

4: Create Instant Rapport

*R*apport *can be summed up in one powerful word: connection.*
Personally relating to another human being in such a manner that you
become "bridged." Your combined presence becomes something of a
celebration, a joy to share in, and a welcoming, inviting milieu is created that's
simple and fun. You're connected in thought, connected in emotion, and you
understand each other's experience of the present moment. Absent of judgment, rapport is more like a heartbeat than a technique. You "click" with each
other.

Rapport is one of the most fascinating aspects of human behavior to see set
in motion. Any barriers relating to one another simply drop.

Neurolinguistic programming, or NLP, teaches us a deliberate method to
establish rapport. In NLP, you match a person's "representational system" by
ascertaining through eye movements if they are visual, auditory or kinesthetic
(feeling type) communicators by nature. Once you determine that, you relate
to that person using their favored type of communication style. For example, if
you determine that someone is visual in nature, you use words and phrases in
your conversation to match that, such as, "I *see* what you're saying," or "Can
you *picture* that?" If you determine they are auditory in nature you use words
that reflect that sense as well, for instance, "I like the *sound* of that," or "Does
that *ring* true for you?" We watch eye movements and mimic body posture all
in an effort to build and establish rapport, to feel connected — and it works.

Although these are very valuable and useful techniques, none of these
experiences taught me the potency of rapport more than my interaction with a
single child. Her name was Shaneka. She had just turned three years old the
day before we met in the emergency room at Larkin General Hospital in Miami.

(Shaneka has been the youngest child to favorably respond to my approach in an emergency setting.) She had fallen, playing outside, and had cut her face, requiring stitches over her eye. I remember working alone with her as her babysitter was squeamish and wanted to wait in the waiting room. Shaneka was a happy child with stars for eyes, and had little idea why she was in the ER or what needed to be done. I took my time to warm up to her and become friends, as a decline in patient flow allowed me the time and the opportunity. She was talkative and friendly during our casual conversation as I lifted her tiny body up to the stretcher, staying by her side. Stretchers can be fun to stand on too, because you can bounce your knees up and down while you hold onto the side rails and talk and ask a lot of questions all at the same time.

"Will you play a game with me?" I asked. She stopped bouncing for a moment and smiled at my eyes.

"What?" she said.

Well, during our little conversation I discovered she liked to watch a lot of *Sesame Street* reruns and talk about the characters. Fortunately, I was familiar with them, having a daughter myself. So that's what we did. We talked about all our favorite characters and their silly antics, only the game was played *lying down* on the stretcher with a sterile field over your face and your eyes closed! It has been my experience with children, that when they close their eyes you get an automatic corresponding physical state of relaxation as well. This seems to be natural and rather spontaneous for them. This is not so with adults. For adults, it's a distinct two-step process of eye closure and then body relaxation. Children save you a step.

Shaneka was progressing nicely in our work together, barely moving while we played our game intently, describing in intimate detail the characters and their distinct personalities. All of the bounding physical energy she came in with was successfully redirected into concentrated and detailed imagery, and imagine and talk we did, as I watched the paper sterile field slightly move in rhythm beneath her breath. She held very still as part of our "game," and kept her hands at her side while the physician laid sterile drapes over her face, cleaned out the laceration, and inserted a needle into her wound to anesthetize it before suturing it closed. Because her imagination was so highly engaged, three-year-old Shaneka never moved — except her mouth, of course, as she continued talking and imagining with me. In those moments together, I was neither her nurse, nor her my patient. We were innocent playmates. The physician took advantage of the situation working quickly and silently (two favorites of any seasoned ER doc) not wanting to interrupt the obvious flow. Nearing the end though, he did chime in adding a character or two that we neglected to mention. What proceeded next is the highlight of the story!

As we were wrapping things up with her wound, and completed the procedure, the doctor removed the sterile field from Shaneka's face proudly announcing, "We're all done, you can get up now."

Do you know what she did next? Absolutely nothing! She didn't respond to the doctor at all. He was completely ignored — chopped liver. She remained lying there in that same posture, silent and unmoving with her eyes still closed! I was in awe just looking at this innocent little child still in rapport because our game was not over yet as far as she was concerned. She was waiting for *me* to tell her it was all over before she was going anywhere. Now that's rapport! The pause and surprise on the doctor's face was absolutely priceless. He looked at her, and then he looked at me, shook his head and just smiled.

"Okay, we're all done now," I said, as she immediately sat up and put her fingers all over the doctor's work. Emergency rooms and stitches can be a lot more fun than a baby-sitter and a bike ride if you know how to play the game.

Yes, I have read, studied and practiced techniques of rapport and its importance, but I had never felt its impact on such a gut level before. Intellectual knowledge is impotent without works. Ideas and concepts can be intellectually stimulating, but when put into practice the realism is totally exhilarating. All that I know about what *really* constitutes rapport I learned from a three-year-old. When the student is ready, the teacher will come!

Tips for Creating Instant Rapport with Children

1) Find out the child's interests, and engage them in a detailed conversation about the things they like to do the most. Hobbies, sports, television programs, cartoons and computer games are a good place to start to find

out what interests them. If they're shy, talk about the things you like to do to get the idea started. Just make sure you describe something they can understand or relate to according to their age group.

2) Never underestimate the active imagination of a child, and their ability to engage it in a playful fashion that deepens rapport with you at the same time.

3) Create a positive association with your presence by smiling, having a little fun or giving them something to play with. Make brief, frequent, friendly contact so when they're in your presence, you're perceived as nonthreatening.

4) Consider combining rapport with playing a game tailored to the type of cooperation you need from the child. For example, ask the child to close their eyes and pretend a bird has landed on their arm. Tell them to hold very still and talk quietly so the bird stays on their arm and doesn't fly away so you can look at him more closely. Ask them to describe what they see, as you perpetuate the game and elicit the details of the experience they imagine.

5) Creatively play with medical equipment the child is afraid of. For example, I once placed an oxygen mask a child was afraid to put on their face, on my head and pretended it was a hat! It interrupted the pattern of fear, and initiated rapport.

6) Have a dress-up party. Together, put on surgical gowns, masks, gloves, hair caps and shoe covers. Give them your stethoscope and show them how to listen to heart sounds.

7) Use humor if it comes naturally to you, but make sure it's appropriate at the time.

8) Relax, just be yourself and have fun when you practice connecting with kids facing minor challenges. Then graduate to bigger ones.

Born out of the natural consequence of lovingly sharing who you are, rapport is simple, honest and open while having the other person's best interest in mind. It can be seen in gentle, inviting eye contact, heard in the tone of the spoken words and experienced physically as a sense of comfort when in close proximity to each other. Rapport is enthusiastic and has a sense of urgency, wanting to share all of who you are immediately. Perhaps it has the energy of spirit — spiritual in the sense that there is no perceived boundary between the two of you as far as you're concerned. It's not that boundaries have been removed, they never existed in you in the first place. The meeting with the other is an extension of yourself. "All one," as the saying goes. How can the other person not feel the warmth, the invitation, and be drawn in by your very presence to reflect the same?

It's important not to ask *how* to establish rapport. It's more important to just completely want it on your end. Rapport is so simple, it's not hard at all, and it can be immediate even with someone you don't know. For example, I was walking Tom, a patient I just met, back to my office from the waiting room. The very first thing he said to me was, "The only reason I came to the Diabetes Center for education today is because my doctor made me come."

"I'm glad you came," I said.

As we were walking down the corridor, he said to me rather defiantly, "I don't have diabetes — and I don't want it either!"

I had all his laboratory values from the doctor, which was evidence enough. He had two elevated fasting blood sugars over 126 and a high hemoglobin A1C value, both confirming his diagnosis. I knew millions of individuals new to type 2 diabetes don't even have any symptoms. These three facts were ammunition enough to counter his statement, and to make him see things my way as an effort to help him break through his apparent state of denial. But rapport also means coming completely from the other person's perspective, and that is exactly how I responded.

"I don't blame you," I said, as we continued walking. "I wouldn't want to be told I had diabetes either unless it was absolutely certain."

We sat down in my office, as his arms defensively crossed over his chest.

"And I don't have any symptoms either," he continued.

"Then it's hard to believe anything is wrong at all," I said.

67

Immediately he uncrossed his arms and moved to a more open body position. He leaned forward and actually grabbed his chair and shifted it closer to me. He disarmed himself. Rapport came alive within the short time it took to walk from the waiting room to my office. Both of my statements to him were nothing more than an exact reflection of what he told me he was thinking and feeling in the moment. I joined with *his* perspective, not mine. He knew then that I was not out to change or challenge his beliefs, rather I was present to understand his own. There was nothing to protect against, nothing to defend. We shared the same view emotionally and mentally. The connection was made and we had instant rapport. It took only two or three interactive sentences to see the man start to make an internal shift in the way he chose to relate to me.

Forty minutes later, the same man who didn't believe he had diabetes, and came to see me because his doctor made him, decided he wanted to attend a five-week diabetes self-care course. He made it very clear to me, however, that he only wanted to attend the class that I was teaching.

Tips for Creating Instant Rapport with Adults

1) Start your interaction with the intention that you are going to find a way to connect with this person even before you begin to work with them.

2) Practice coming entirely from the other person's perspective, both emotionally and mentally, to build rapport. Reflect back to them how they are thinking and especially how they are feeling. Be genuine and sincere in all your interactions. Adults will open up and respond much more in a non-judgmental environment. Humor can create an immediate bond but make sure it's used appropriately.

3) Give the person your full attention. Lean forward toward them.

4) Maintain good eye contact. Continue that eye contact as long as you can during distractions like phones, pagers and interruptions from other people, so you give the impression they are more important than those distractions.

5) Repeat the words or phrases they say that you believe carry importance for

them. Repeat them exactly as they stated it, word for word, so they understand you heard them. Make affirmative statements and sounds like *yes, um hum,* to stay engaged.

6) Maintain an open body posture yourself. Don't cross your arms or even your legs if you're sitting at a table. Nod your head to acknowledge you're listening.

7) Play with building your rapport skills with people you briefly interact with during normal daily activities, e.g., store clerks, neighbors, strangers.

8) Rapport breakers would include bad breath, not being honest, creating power struggles, having answers for everything, staring, looking at your watch, giving misinformation, being late, and giving computers or phones too much attention.

With children, rapport can be even faster than the example of Tom that I just gave you because they're so spontaneous. That way of being is so naturally inherent to them. It's not so much an intellectual exchange for children as it is an energetic or intuitive one. Harder to explain or define perhaps, but powerfully present nevertheless. You are at an advantage with children because rapport with them just tends to be more immediate by their very nature. You walk into the room and their willingness to work with you is already decided by how they perceive the look on your face, the light in your eyes and the expression carried in your heart. Children see all that immediately and intuitively respond to their impression of you.

> *A little girl was talking to her teacher about whales. The teacher said it was physically impossible for a whale to swallow a human because even though they were a very large mammal their throat was very small.*
>
> *The little girl stated that Jonah was swallowed by a whale. The teacher reiterated that a whale could not swallow a human; it was impossible.*
>
> *The little girl said, "When I get to heaven I will ask Jonah."*

The teacher asked, "What if Jonah went to hell?"
The little girl replied, "Then you ask him!"

Children have a way of knowing where your heart is.

My wife was once asked how many children she had and she responded, "Two — my daughter and my husband!" Rapport with children comes easy to those who express innocence and know the joy of just wanting to have some fun even in a medical setting. When you can come from the space of just being a kid yourself, there exists no gap in your connection to each other. The play-fulness is immediately recognized.

Have you ever seen a group of children together for the first time who don't know each other and just start playing? I find that same type of connection exists between adults and children as well. Perhaps the biblical saying, "Only those who are like children will enter the kingdom," epitomizes that which binds us most — qualities of innocence and playfulness.

Never underestimate two simple, and what appear to be universal, truths when children are involved. One, their active imagination and how powerfully they can naturally engage it; and two, the impact your authority has on determining expectations, reactions and outcomes.

I would not have remained in the nursing profession for thirty years unless fun and playfulness were involved in the mix. Experience gives you the wisdom to know when you can introduce it appropriately. Creating fun and playfulness with children in a medical setting is a lot more valuable and appropriate than we were taught in nursing school. Come to think of it, we weren't taught about its value at all! Being too serious has probably gotten me into more trouble than being playful and spontaneous.

As any professional in uniform, you represent and implicate tremendous meaning. Your presence alone, your clothes alone, symbolize an unspoken intention. Remember, as a nurse you possess an extraordinary advantage quite naturally to develop rapport. Webster himself defines us as those who "cure or treat, or take special care of." You're viewed as an expert and receive a natural form of attention in the eyes of the public.

You do this work every day, so you know what to expect and what usually happens. More importantly, you know how *it's supposed to happen.* Just through this one simple basic understanding alone, I have literally talked scores of kids into their experiences. Step by step, how it will unfold right down to the reaction, right down to the response, right down to the giggle. So many children are fearful of even a drop of blood, especially their own, and many more times afraid of just the very idea of it!

I remember when I was about five years old, and I pinched my finger playing on a swing set with my cousins. A tiny spot of blood the size of a pinhead popped up, and I started running around crying, "Don't take me to the hospital, don't take me to the hospital." I recall this overreaction so vividly. Blood triggered fear, which was directly associated with hospitals, which I also feared. Getting unnecessarily carried away seemed like the right thing to do for me at the time, and I understood this reasoning perfectly.

Sometimes, there is no other way than the hard way to do your work. Often times, young children need time to realize they don't have a choice in getting injections, getting blood drawn, and having their fingers lanced.

Jamie was one such five-year-old. She was newly diagnosed with type 1 diabetes. Blood sugar checks along with insulin injections, were to be done every four hours during her initial hospital admission. The pediatric staff nurses caring for her described to me all they were going through with her because of her phobia and dreaded repeat performances on a four-hour basis. Jamie ran from them, hid from them and fought with them. Her ear-piercing screams were the hardest part to endure.

The nursing staff was relieved to see me coming. Not only because I was the nurse educator from the Diabetes Center, but also because two exasperated nurses at exactly the same time said, "It's your turn."

Right around the time of this experience, the industry came out with an adjustable lancing device that could be set to various levels of skin penetration to obtain fingertip blood samples. What I didn't know was that today it would be given a nickname.

As I approached the entrance to her room, Jamie ran into the arms of her mother.

"Hello," I said, smiling, while making what eye contact I could with Jamie. She reciprocated by burying her face further in her mother's belly attempting to hide from me.

"I brought you a present," I said, handing her the device still new in the box, and laying it on the bed next to her when she refused to take it from me.

I always try to make eye contact with the child first when I enter the room and then with the parents. To me it's a way of setting the priority of whom I'm there for in establishing rapport. After complimenting Jamie on her pretty dress, I moved my attention to her parents. We talked for a little while about the implications of her diagnosis. Eventually Jamie's curiosity got the best of her because she wanted to know what this friendly stranger had brought her and opened the box.

"It works like this," I said, showing her how to unscrew the top and how to push the big blue button, which made a loud click. "It's called a laughing stick," I said, (spontaneously and out of the blue) repeating that phrase several times, "so don't laugh when you use it." She shot a disbelieving glance back at me, briefly looking into my eyes for the first time. "Don't laugh when you use it now," I repeated, as a thin, careful smile skipped across her face. Again, I moved my attention off her and back onto the parents as we talked about the basic pathophysiology of diabetes. Out of the corner of my eye I watched as Jamie grew even more curious now, then began screwing the cap on and off and pushing the blue button which triggered the empty device over and over.

"This equipment is completely different from anything the hospital uses, and I promise Jamie will like it," I said. "But don't laugh when you use it now," I kept repeating with a smile as I returned my attention to her. "You have to promise not to laugh."

Once you see in a child's face a moment of pause, an attempted smile, or even a look of doubt or confusion, that's the moment to verbally interject exactly what you want the child to do. Learn to recognize these moments as fertile ground for them to receive your suggestions. Tell them how to do what you want them to do. Condense, encapsulate in a few simple words or sentences how they will feel, react, and experience your interaction with them and then repeat those statements over and over. They will learn to make a positive association with your presence and with this phrase in an almost game-like fashion. With Jamie, I became the nurse she would later associate with as the "laughing-stick guy" and the "don't-laugh-when-you-use-it guy."

Well, naturally after having established a little rapport, and hearing over and over how easy this would be, and asking her to promise not to laugh, that's the very first thing she did! The most uncooperative child on the ward picked up the now-loaded device, and by herself lanced her own finger and actually laughed at the moment of impact. Enough of a blood sample was available to test without repeating any of her previous negative responses. Her face lit up with surprise and delight at having done this by herself. Her cycle of fear was finally broken and the laughing stick was born.

Yes, it was "my turn," to enjoy this work today and add Jamie to that invisible group of children who stand behind me every time I work face to face with a new frightened child.

When I returned to my department, I shared the story with a coworker. She actually didn't believe me when I told her that Jamie laughed during the procedure. Again, can you see how your perspective dramatically influences outcomes? Had this educator worked with Jamie, the possibilities for the child would have become more narrowed. Laughter would not have been among those possibilities. Her intention, rapport and the expectations she might have created would all have been affected.

Think with me for a moment, if you will, of all the changes that might take place for a child when they have a positive experience. An encounter such as this shapes how they feel about hospitals, doctors and nurses. Their feelings about themselves and their ability to face fear alter dramatically. This is one of the experiences they will carry and remember as they enter into a new phase of their life being diagnosed with a chronic medical condition. One person can make a difference. You and I can make a small difference in building a lasting impression because oftentimes, small and determined is all it takes.

SUMMARY

1) Never underestimate how something as simple as a little rapport with someone can completely change your interactions with them and their willingness to cooperate with you.

2) Begin to notice the current communication style you use to reach people to develop a feeling of rapport. What can you change or fine-tune to make it even better? Consider combining your intention with whatever inherent skill you have to build an immediate, friendly relationship with the adults and children with whom you're working.

3) Recognize the power you can harness from a child's natural inclination for an overactive imagination. Realize the extent children can engage that imagination as an avenue for you to create trust and rapport.

4) Bond with children while letting them safely play with whatever piece of medical equipment or object they are afraid of, while you're supervising them.

5) Reread the tips for rapport and experiment with them one at a time. Find the one that feels most natural and works best for you in finding your immediate connection with the children.

6) When no one is looking (and especially when they are), act like a kid yourself!

You walk into the room and their willingness to work with you is already decided by how they perceive the look on your face, the light in your eyes and the expression carried in your heart.

Children have a way of knowing where your heart is.

—•— ⟨◊⟩ —•—

"I know you understand what you think I said,
but I'm not sure you realize that what you
heard is not what I meant."
–Richard McQulleon

—•— ⟨◊⟩ —•—

5: Use Proper Semantics

*S*emantics *refers to the meaning we create through the specific* words we use. To create the meaning you are aiming for, *word choice* becomes critical. All spoken words with children are best used in the positive sense, stating what you *want* to happen, not what you don't want to happen.

For example, "Don't move" would be an example of improper semantics. "Hold still," is saying the same thing from a positive sense and at the same time you're now describing what you want.

Behaviorists describe an observed phenomenon, which occurs as an automatic subconscious function, where the negative aspect or word is dropped in a stated phrase. So in the sentence "Don't move," the word "Don't" is dropped, and the patient hears the word "move." I once heard of an NLP experiment performed in which thirty school children were given a carton of milk with the instructions, "Don't spill your milk." Three of the children spilled it. The experiment was repeated again, this time with the statement, "Be careful with your milk." None was spilled!

Construct your sentence to match your intentions and the expectations you're aiming to create. Further, when intentions, expectations and proper semantics are combined and sending the same message, yet another law of the power of suggestion comes into play — the Law of Compounding. Repeating the same suggestion, again and again in different ways, through different forms of expression, strengthens it, and increases the likelihood it will be accepted and followed. Watch your words and your specific word choices for they are powerful!

For example, I was working with Greg, an eight-year-old boy, in the emergency room. Greg needed extensive work on a serious leg wound, as well as local anesthetizing and extensive suturing. I wasn't sure if he wanted to work with me or not. His fear was overwhelming as he looked into my eyes with a strong sense of distrust. He seemed to believe there was no other way that the work could possibly be done without experiencing a lot of pain. He was sitting up on the stretcher and huddled over his leg in a protective, defensive posture. Greg had little to say and wasn't very willing to follow any of my advice. I remember the time it took to slowly break through his repetitious, fearful thought pattern and replace it with something more favorable.

Semantically, I repeated, "Relax your leg like it's sound asleep. Relax your leg like it's sound asleep." Eventually, I gained enough of his trust that he took his eyes off me and looked at his leg in a partial attempt to follow my instructions. *Finally...* I thought to myself.

"If you make your leg very still just like you're doing now, and close your eyes and think about something you enjoy doing, together we can make this a comfortable experience for you," I said.

Since his greatest fear was pain, I also repeated the word *comfortable* in many of my sentences. As I prepared the room for the doctor, I could tell by the boy's relaxed physical body posture, the tone of his voice and his willingness to lie down on the stretcher, that much of his fear had subsided. He was slowly shifting into trust.

Just then the doctor walked into the room. He talked with the patient for a moment and then sat down on a stool at the foot of the bed.

"When I inject your leg to make it numb you're going to feel *pain*," he said.

Immediately, the boy bolted upright on the stretcher, as all his fear returned.

"What?" he said. One word alone was enough to dismantle the expectations and trust that this boy and I had worked so hard to create.

The doctor immediately realized his poor choice of words. I had spent so much time working with Greg's fear that I didn't get to the doctor in time to tell him what was going on. "We are going to make this as *comfortable* as possible," would have been a much better choice of words. Remarkably, however, the doctor and I were able to recover enough to regain his cooperation and convince this boy that his experience would be a good one. It took a little more time to get his confidence and trust back, but we salvaged his positive experience. I attributed that to two things: my rapport with the child and teamwork with the doctor. A physician's word will always supercede a nurse's word. Working together, reinforcing the same message as a team, always produces the best results because this consistency engages the law of compounding. Greg needed to hear the same word choice over and over from different people to loosen his grip on fear. What we both learned in our experience with Greg is that sometimes we have so much influence on a patient's experience that they literally hang on our every word. Using words wisely is wise indeed.

Fellow professionals have often questioned my approach saying, "But it *does* hurt to stick a needle several times in an open wound! I don't want to lie to them." What they all come to realize after I remind them of what they already know, is the basic fact that pain is subjective. Individuals have different thresholds of pain. Thresholds can be influenced.

Just because your experience is painful does not mean someone else's has to be. I have seen countless times how rapport, imagery, and the power of expectations can block pain effectively. I have also seen analgesics rendered completely ineffective when the patient's fear was never addressed. Give the children and the people you work with these supportive tools and then let them decide for themselves. But remember, the children will be aware of what it is that you anticipate. You can't just go through the motions with these suggestions even if they're technically correct. You have to believe in your combined abilities to create a comfortable experience. It always comes back to you and the clarity of your intentions.

I'll share another example of how even a single word can impact a patient's perception. When my daughter Nicole was seventeen, I was helping her change her bandages at home. She had fallen off a motorcycle on the expressway and had to have bedside orthopedic surgery on her knee.

I looked at her wound and said, "You're healing nicely. That one stitch looks *buried*." All I meant was that healing tissue was growing very well. Apparently, she associated the word buried with difficulty removing the stitch.

"Buried?" she repeated loudly. "What do you mean buried?" She got mad at me saying that she wasn't sure she wanted my help changing her bandages anymore.

"The next time, I'm going to ask Mom for help instead of you," she said. That night when she went to sleep, she was still complaining about my word choice. I had to apologize and repeat my explanation several times until I was forgiven!

It is especially important with toddlers and preschool children ages three through five to not only choose your words carefully but to explain what you mean by them. Children in this age bracket will take you literally and innocently believe, for instance, that a CAT scan has something to do with cats. I even heard a coworker tell a story about how a child misunderstood the word "diabetes." The child literally believed she would "Die from the bee tees." In this age group keep your words simple, and explain them thoroughly to avoid a potential misunderstanding. A plastic surgeon I met told me two words he never uses in surgery even with adults when under local anesthesia when they can hear everything. "Uh-oh" and "Whoops!"

An Exercise in Semantics

In an effort to understand how powerful semantics are and the impact words can have on your perceptions, try this exercise. Practice listening to the words you use when you're talking to someone and describing a situation in your life that you may find difficult to deal with or find personally challenging. Pay close attention to what you're saying, the words you are using and how you say them. Using a Zen-type approach, lovingly observe your words without judgment so you become familiar with the exact phrases you're feeding yourself. In the beginning, it's important that you don't tell yourself these are good or bad statements. Just get to know what these statements are in their raw form without any labeling or antagonism on your part. If you discover your word

Nicole, Age 17

choices are negative, you just may have discovered for yourself why these situations are so challenging. Semantically, you keep reinforcing a negative experience.

The first part of this exercise is simply to become more aware of what you're saying to yourself. Once you have clearly identified that, start intentionally changing what you're verbally feeding yourself. We're concerned about what we feed our bodies, so why shouldn't we be equally concerned about what we feed our hearts and minds through our spoken words? By becoming aware of our "verbal diet," and intentionally changing the words to more positive statements, we enter into new thought patterns. Our thought patterns enter our belief systems. Our belief systems join forces with our subconscious, and a new, well-defined, restructured pattern of thinking, believing and responding becomes established. Pay attention to the type of words and statements you're focusing on, for they become your reality. Sayings like, "He's going to eat those words," are not by coincidence. You're slowly digesting and integrating their intended meaning.

Counter One Negative Statement with Two Positive Ones

When I first started sharing these skills with friends at work, we turned it into a game. On the days I worked triage in the emergency department, I worked right alongside Candace, a member of the registration staff. We became friends, laughing over the bizarre and funny things that happened there. I noticed how she would verbally put herself down and use a lot of negative self-talk.

She would say things to me like, "I knew that was a stupid thing to do, and it figures I would be the one to do it," or, "I'm not smart enough to get it right the first time."

When I first brought her attention to what she was saying, I don't think she realized the extent of her self-sabotage, and the frequency with which she took verbal shots at herself. Yet she was the most delightful person to be around. Candace had a brilliant sense of humor, her coworkers loved her, and she obviously enjoyed being with people.

"Every time you put yourself down with one hard statement," I said, "you have to say two things you're good at or like about yourself."

At first, it took a little time for her to really become aware of what she was automatically saying to herself. It took even longer for her to come up with two positive counter statements. Finally, one day when she was upset with herself, she accidentally walked past me in the middle of delivering a hard, verbal blow against herself.

She stopped, looked at me and without hesitation said, "Okay, I do a great job registering patients, and I have a good sense of humor." We both laughed. In a short amount of time with practicing this exercise, she stopped beating herself up verbally and her word choice became much more positive.

Take this exercise a step further and do it with your thought process. Play the same game and create more positive thinking by countering negative thoughts. The key to enjoying this whole process is to just relax into being more aware. The results will come as a natural consequence. Once you discover the impact this exercise has on you personally, it's easier to see how your word choice can affect others.

Refining Your Semantics

The easiest way to remember how to properly word your statements is to say what you want, not what you don't want, as I mentioned earlier. "It won't *hurt*," becomes "We can make this *comfortable*." "I hope he doesn't *fight* with me," becomes "I'll encourage *cooperation*." "Don't *move*," becomes "Hold *still*." Never start a sentence with the word "Don't..."

Choose words and phrases that best describe and reinforce the positive expectations you are trying to create. Repeat those words or phrases frequently throughout your interaction with the child. Remember, younger children may take you literally!

Communicate to the doctor the positive key words or phrases you're using with the child. Ask the doctor to say them in front of the child as well so the message becomes reinforced.

Repeat the child's own positive phrases in their exact words if you hear them using any.

Ask your coworkers to observe how they hear you speak in front of children and especially in front of frightened children. Consider their feedback.

Practice replacing negatively stated words during routine conversations with friends.

The Power of the Spoken Word

Our spoken word carries tremendous power and commitment. Business contracts and major negotiations are often initiated by the power of our spoken word. Saying things such as, "Do I have your word on that?" or, "He's good for his word," imply an understood meaning between two parties. How many business deals are made on the golf course through spoken agreements alone?

One day while building our house in North Carolina, I overheard the local workers talking. "He doesn't go by your word," said Gary, who was doing our structural framing and talking to the grader.

They were talking about me, because I wanted all agreements to be in writing. We had moved from Miami, Florida, to Asheville, North Carolina, and it seemed in this area verbal agreements were customary, and a man's word continued to hold high meaning. A man's word was (and still is) his honorable contract in this part of the country. In fact, this had been part of the reason my family and I had moved to Asheville in the first place. I thought to myself, Okay, if that's how they do things here... So a word and a handshake was all I needed to build our house. My friends from Miami thought I was crazy! I can't tell you the pride I experienced while playing general contractor. I wrote all the verbal quotes for estimates in a green wire-bound tablet, and a lot of them were over the phone, not even face to face! Not all of them with a handshake either, just a man's word. What I came to realize is how powerfully the spoken word still exists in this part of the country, and is part of the pride of their heritage. The highlight of my experience was handing a check written down to the penny to one of two brothers who did the insulation. I wrote it out before he asked for final payment. We just grinned at each other when he handed me the bill with one hand, and at the same time I handed him the check for the exact amount with the other. From the ground up to moving in, all my contracts with workers were verbal agreements, and not a single word was broken. This experience dynamically strengthened what I already knew to be true. Your words are powerful.

How Other Cultures View the Spoken Word

Author Catherine Ponder, in her book *The Dynamic Laws of Healing*, explains how other cultures view the spoken word. Babylonians taught that a word is a command or promise, which is bound to come true. A prevalent teaching in Hindu scripture is that the word is all-powerful. Greeks for centuries have taught that the word is substance itself containing a cosmic power to build up or tear down. The Oriental race believed that through the dynamics of sound, every spoken word has tremendous power, a vibratory force that profoundly affects physical substance. The Egyptian culture taught that words used as affirmations helped healing to occur by stimulating centers of consciousness. In our own culture, the Bible is referred to as The Word.

I shared some of these thoughts with Kevin, a friend of mine who is a dentist, and he decided to test my theory. He told me he couldn't believe the impact he made on his patients by simply changing what he told them before dental procedures.

"If I told them they were going to have a comfortable experience today, they did," he said. "All it took was my saying so," he declared with surprise. "I never realized how much influence my words alone were having on my patients," he continued.

Kevin shared two experiences with me he found hard to believe himself, since he was a man of science. One was suggesting to a patient that his headache would probably subside rather quickly. "It actually did," he said.

The other story brought tears to his eyes. He and his wife had a dog that was battling a long-term illness. "There are times I think that dog is so loyal that he is afraid to die because he knows how much we love him and will miss him, and he's holding on for our sake," he said.

He asked my advice. I suggested kneeling down and making eye contact with his dog, and telling him you and your wife will be okay if he needs to pass on. That you understand, and you will be all right. I was introducing the Oriental belief that the vibratory tone of those heartfelt words have a way of being understood even in the animal kingdom.

I saw Kevin a week later, and with tears in his eyes, he told me that in less than twenty-four hours after doing this, his dog passed away. Neither of us entertained the coincidence theory.

What I'm saying is that there are laws of nature not scientifically understood, but this does not negate the fact that forms of communication can and do occur even in the animal kingdom through the spoken word.

Apply these ideas wholeheartedly and decide for yourself how powerful they are. Be experimental.

Your Words Are Remembered

Audrey, a nine-year-old girl, was sitting up in her hospital bed when I approached. Her mom had gone to the cafeteria to take a coffee break. Audrey was newly diagnosed with type 1 diabetes and needed to learn how to draw blood from her finger to test her blood sugar, and then measure and inject insulin. At first she was unsure she could do all that but displayed an openness and a willingness that I wanted to act on right then and there. She exuded a keen sense of intelligence, and we instantly established trust and rapport.

Throughout our interaction I repeatedly told her, "You are smart, and learn new things easily." In the time it took her mother to go downstairs to the cafeteria for a cup of coffee and return, Audrey had already overcome her doubts and demonstrated all the following: how to lance her finger and express enough blood for glucose testing; operation of the glucose meter; how to calibrate and set up the glucose meter to receive the blood sample; and how to withdraw, measure and store insulin and proper techniques for self-injection.

She learned all the places she could administer her own injections and even gave herself a shot of sterile saline for practice. I felt as though we had participated in a fifty-yard dash and that she was absorbing and retaining the information as fast as I could give it.

Not only were the functional skills imparted very quickly, but her understanding of the disease state went amazingly well over the course of her hospital admission as well. Ironically, her discharge was delayed a day because neither parent was as up to speed as their child was. The rapport Audrey and I experienced together was on the fast track. I remember reinforcing repeatedly how smart she was and how easily she would learn the new skills. She beamed with delight upon hearing me say those words, and I reinforced them with each new skill I taught her.

Her family moved shortly afterward, and I didn't see her for several years. Then one day, Audrey and her mom came to visit me at the Diabetes Center, just to say hello and reconnect. Audrey repeated the *exact* same phrase to me during our conversation I had used to encourage her learning when I met her five years ago.

She talked about her new school and said to me, "I'm smart, and learn new things easily." Her mom wanted to thank me for being instrumental at a key turning point in both her life and her daughter's life. It was inspiring to see Audrey take the skills she learned that day and apply them to her life as a fourteen-year-old. I could never have imagined one simple loving interaction, combined with the words I used, having such a lasting effect.

Audrey never seemed to doubt just how smart she was, and that seemed like intelligence in and of itself to me. Because she had "learned new things easily," at a critical moment in her life, she seemed to find it even easier to apply that same belief pattern elsewhere in her life. Those key words made a lasting impression, and Audrey made it clear to me our brief relationship had been very meaningful to her.

Would you not agree how easily you can recall the words people have said to you in your own life during a moment of high emotional impact? Whether your experience was favorable or otherwise, those words are hard to forget. The right words in the right moment have a way of staying with you. Hence the power of properly applied semantics.

NLP also teaches that if you can use the right word to describe exactly what you're experiencing inside as you're experiencing it, you become a master communicator. As the saying goes, "If they don't get it, you ain't got it!" Get it?

When we as healthcare providers say what we mean and mean what we say, then we become more believable to those we work with. Our patients hear it, beyond the words and into the meaning, which takes us back to our intention again. When I tell a child they are going to have a great experience, I know it and believe it. I've seen it...and I want it to happen to them. It is not a casual statement. It's pregnant with meaning, and that's what they hear in our words.

A man is in the hospital lying in bed with an oxygen mask over his face. A young nurse comes into his room to give him a sponge bath.

"Nurse," he mumbles from behind the mask, "are my testicles black?"

Embarrassed, the young nurse replies, "I don't know, I'm just here to give you a sponge bath."

He struggles again and asks, "Nurse, are my testicles black?"

Frustrated, she pulls back the covers, raises his gown, holds his penis in one hand, his testicles in her other hand, and takes a close look and says, "There is nothing wrong with them!"

Finally, the man pulls off his oxygen mask and replies, "That was very nice, nurse, but *are my test results back?*"

As you can see, even with good intentions it will take practice and patience to get good at finding the right words to use. Have fun playing with your semantics.

SUMMARY

1) Recognize the power held in your spoken words and learn how to use them to your advantage.

2) Become more aware of the specific words you're using when confronted with a frightened child. Practice using positively stated phrases rather than negative ones.

3) Review the list of suggestions under Refining Your Semantics and experiment with them to help you build clarity and rapport in your communication.

4) Consider saying two things out loud you like about yourself whenever you say something negative about yourself. Try the same experiment with your thoughts too.

5) Are *you* good for your word? Can people rely on you to do what you say you're going to do without them having to remind you? Only when you are, will you fully understand the power and impact words alone have to offer.

6) Have fun sharing the concept of semantics with friends.

> *When I tell a child they are going to*
> *have a great experience, I know it*
> *and believe it. I've seen it... and I want*
> *it to happen to them. It is not a casual*
> *statement. It's pregnant with meaning,*
> *and that's what they hear in our words.*

"Once you make a decision, the universe
conspires to make it happen."
–Ralph Waldo Emerson

6: Gain Cooperation with Your Initial Approach

*T*he entire purpose of your initial approach is to reduce fear, create positive expectations and gain cooperation. Based on my experience, the three most important skills you can develop to accomplish these goals are your intention, creating a positive association with your presence and establishing rapport.

Your initial approach can be a critical factor in determining the child's total experience. The way you present yourself and interact with children when you first meet them can have a tremendous impact on the outcome of your intervention and the level of cooperation they will choose to give you. This is a key moment to alter the child's perception of the situation and their level of fear. At that first contact, you have the opportunity to start and set the pace for how the medical intervention and the child's response to it will unfold.

Start with Your Intention

The first step is, and will always be, your intention. Where you are internally is going to drive your initial approach. The intention you carry will dictate all your actions and responses. All that you're thinking, feeling and anticipating is going to be nonverbally revealed as you step into that room. When you become aware of what that is for you, your successes will come more naturally. Your first responsibility to the child is to be responsible with where you stand within yourself.

Ideally, your intention is to take whatever you're given to work with and create the best possible outcome for the child. To see to it that, through you,

Haley, Age 7

they have a favorable, positive experience. Your intention is to connect with them in such a way as to empower the child with that very same interpretation of the experience. Together, you're going to make it happen. You are excited about meeting them, and you look forward to sharing your spirited conviction and determination in seeing that reality unfold.

Through your intention, you have already started your connection with the child whether you're in their presence or not. They will sense on some level the mindset you've put into motion within yourself. This in turn will have an effect on them from the minute they meet you.

Realize that the most powerful first message you send is nonverbal, even if you come into the room talking. A human being, who is under some degree of duress by being placed in a medical environment and in a vulnerable position, is instinctively and by design going to evaluate and react to a host of inputs, not just words. You will be evaluated head to toe immediately.

NLP teaches that as many as eight decisions are made about a person you meet within the first seventeen seconds. You will summarize instantaneously your likes and dislikes about a person. The way they walk, talk, look, dress and respond. Their eye contact, attitude, tone of voice and facial expressions are examined, reviewed and decided upon instinctively.

Through your intention, you can deliberately create your first message, and it is the most powerful one you can send because it's the foundation of your behavior and beliefs.

By approaching children with a clear intention, you begin to take full responsibility for creating their experience. As a professional, you have that much power to make it happen for them. When you begin to place that kind of confidence in yourself your patients will see that confidence. Your approach now becomes one of mastery — mastery of yourself and what you would choose to create. This approach is completely independent of circumstances, obstacles and barriers. It's not that obstacles don't exist. They may very well, but they no longer dictate or unduly influence your vision of seeing that child find a way to a positive experience in your presence nevertheless.

There is a vast difference in this approach compared to entering the room with a let's-see-what-happens attitude. When chance or fate become your intention, you completely disempower yourself and your patient. Ultimately, you remove your responsibility and you become more willing to accept failure. You want much more determination than that.

Use your initial approach to immediately begin to teach the child that he or she is not an idle player or a victim to any medical intervention. Together the both of you will team up to create a positive experience.

So be clear as to what you choose to create. Begin to operate with full awareness from the choice you decide upon from the very beginning.

This internal preparation, before you have even set foot in the room, is the source of your success. You're most likely doing this to some degree already, but you may not be fully aware of your internal positioning; or perhaps you place little importance on acknowledging its potential impact. When your intention has a clear vision, *you* decide how the interaction is going to unfold, not the surrounding circumstances, and not the child's fear. An intention that determined is the first thing you want to bring to your interaction with the child. You have to set up expectations of your own behavior before you can help with anyone else's. So, before you check on the child, check in on yourself.

With a proper intention set in motion, all of your nonverbal messages will easily fall into place as a natural consequence. With your heart in the right place, you will carry yourself in a relaxed manner and your approach to the child will be nonthreatening. Your eye contact will be soft and your posture and gesturing will support and carry the same message. Your facial expressions will reflect the way you're thinking and reinforce the entire desired nonverbal communication.

These messages become cumulative. At the very least, the child sees before them an expert, a professional in uniform who is personally comfortable: comfortable with themselves, comfortable in the child's presence and in the situation the both of you are presented with. This calm confidence can be highly contagious and spread quickly to everyone in the room.

Create a Positive Association with Your Presence

Most children under five or six years of age really seem to enjoy animated facial expressions. That's part of the fun and attraction of cartoons. Flat facial affects in a medical setting make many children uncomfortable, so at least greet them with a smile. Personally, I get quite a bit of mileage out of enthusiasm and excitement when entering the room. I like being there with them and convey that enthusiasm with an upbeat approach, like I'm seeing a long-lost friend. High fives (offering my hand up high and hitting theirs) are still popular with me and in seconds, nonverbal, verbal and physical contact is made. If there is any positive response from the child here, such as even a thin smile, I know I have a high percentage of control over the situation. I created that smile and I plan to design the entire outcome favorably from here. Initially, my aim is to create a positive association with my very presence. It can be as simple as this — if the child likes you, they will increase their desire to cooperate with you. So get them to like you, even if they're afraid.

Build Your Rapport

The initial approach has a lot to do with building rapport as well, and rapport as we have discussed can be instantaneous. Kids will respond faster and much more often than adults will. Adults spend an awful lot of time in doubt, questioning and analyzing. You have to negotiate through all that first before working with them. The energy is coming from their head, full of explanation and controversy. You get to bypass all of that working with kids because kids communicate straight from the heart, and sometimes heart moves pretty fast once you have rapport. So don't be surprised if things move along much more quickly in the direction you want them to with few delays in the "Yeah, but—" department. After rapport is established, go straight into creating the expectations of their entire experience. Describe in condensed form not just what's *going* to happen but how they are going to *experience* what happens. From start to finish, briefly describe their entire physical and emotional experience. Tell them how easy it will be for them to go through the procedure they are having (e.g., sutures, spinal taps, reducing dislocations) and the ease with which it can be done with your help and guidance. Show them and tell them what they need to do, and how they need to cooperate to make it easy. Just one taste of guiding a child calmly through fear will make you want to repeat that experience again and again with every child.

Find the Turning Point

Let's take the case of Mark, a six-year-old boy who needed a hand surgeon to repair his ruptured tendons, restore full movement to his fingers and close his wound. His bedside surgery was taking place in the emergency department in a room assigned to me. When I came into his room, he was standing in front of his mother. Mark backed up into the safety of his mother's arms the moment he saw me. He started shaking and concealed his wound, which had been bandaged at triage. His breathing became rapid and shallow as he incoherently rattled off his fears and apprehensions. His sentences were incomplete as he took gulps of air in an effort to talk, breathe and communicate his fears all at the same time. Mark's little body trembled.

I sat down in a chair at a little distance from him so we were at eye level. I also thought if I didn't get too close to him too soon, he would have more of an opportunity to relax a bit in my presence. I wanted to provide a safe distance for him to consider getting to know me. Very softly I whispered, "I know a secret way you can have this done, and it will be so easy." The expression on his face changed slightly as he sensed my sincerity.

"When you lie down on the stretcher make your arm very still like it's asleep." I told him. "When you lie real still and relax your arm, you'll just feel the doctor touching you, that's all." I moved in closer and gently ran my hand up and down his arm lightly touching it. His breathing slowed down. Ahh…the turning point! I could see a hint of curiosity now, which meant his thinking had shifted.

"Let me show you what else to do when you're up here," I continued, as I walked over to the stretcher while tapping on it and inviting him to a trial run-through. I pulled a little step stool next to the stretcher. I did this without looking at him directly, and did it with a smile of confidence. I didn't want my invitation to be interpreted as a challenge, an intimidation or in any way an avenue for him to perpetuate his fear. Slowly and hesitantly, he followed my suggestions and climbed up on the stretcher by himself. His mother's face froze with astonishment. He allowed me to instruct him on what to do when the doctor came in, which was to hold still and relax his hand and arm. To my surprise, little else was needed. Mark shifted to a posture of complete trust immediately. He knew he would be okay with me by his side during the procedure. It's my belief he read my intention clearly enough to grant me that trust. His breathing remained calm even when the hand surgeon arrived, and as the room was set up and the instrumentation prepared. He posed no objection to my continued instructions during his procedure, which was completed in about forty-five minutes. The doctor complimented him on how remarkable he behaved for a six-year-old as he and I, along with his mom, just couldn't stop smiling. Mark went from physically trembling with fear to trust, confidence and self-control. He believed, as I believed, that he could empower himself.

By creating a friendly, positive association with my presence I posed no threat. There was no sense of challenge of wills or insisting on doing things without his involvement.

If your initial approach is not producing cooperation often enough, you probably need to have a closer look at all the messages you're projecting and try reworking them. I have seen far too many healthcare workers use an approach that was too fast, too assertive, or even mildly aggressive. Their biggest mistake, in my opinion, is not taking enough time to connect with the child and to build at least some degree of rapport. Things start to go downhill from there; the child never finds a way to cooperate because they're not properly shown, and the knock-down drag-out battle begins. Then they blame the child! As an experiment, ask a coworker their impression of your facial expressions and nonverbal body language and what they say to the frightened patients when you initially greet them.

My favorite success story, which I entirely attribute to my initial approach, involved a three-year-old girl named Rebecca. She was sitting in her mother's lap and immediately grabbed onto her as soon as I entered the room. She was screaming and crying before I even got there. Rebecca shrieked even louder when she saw me, as she now struggled in her mother's arms in an attempt to distance herself even farther from me. She was out of control. Her mother informed me this agitated state had been going on for some time and that it would get worse when anyone came in the room. The child's blonde, curly hair encircled her chubby cheeks, and she was full of perspiration as tears streamed down her face. Rebecca's bright yellow and blue dress displayed a series of cartoon characters on it. Clearly she wanted nothing to do with me as the struggling and crying intensified while I just stood there looking at her. I turned around and left the room.

A few moments later I returned with a coloring book and a box of crayons. I sat next to her and her mother on the stretcher while the crying continued, and I began to color. I turned the pages and found something I liked, coloring some more. This went on for almost five minutes. She stopped crying. Ahh... the turning point! She grabbed a crayon and started coloring with me. Something in her reaction sensed my presence as safe, and a positive association was made. That initial approach was an effective starting point that ended up as a magical turning point in our relationship. Although she fussed and cried throughout her medical exam, she was no longer so agitated and out of control. Her labs and x-rays were obtained without restraint. Realize it's okay if the child still needs to cry, but physical cooperation is a must. Three-year-old Rebecca's experience progressed far better than it would have, had she not been given an opportunity for a brief, positive interaction.

Children will astound you with their level of cooperation based solely on just liking you or trusting that you're there to help and protect them in some way. Trust is often a lost value among many adults but definitely not with kids. They haven't been talked out of it yet. Our unsafe world leads us as parents to protect and over-protect at every contingency. It's good to see trust so alive and thriving in the souls of those children. Working next to them keeps alive in me that blessing and serves as a constant reminder of the power of that trust.

Techniques can help too, as long as your approach is heartfelt while you're applying them. If you use them cunningly, or with too much ego, they almost never work well. When initially approaching a child, remember to use the mirror technique. What do all your nonverbals say? Have a good look at the expression on your face, the message in your eyes, your body posture, and your thoughts and emotions. How is your physical energy level, your affect and intention? Remember how easily children internalize things and that they may believe they are the cause of any uncomfortable emotions you have yourself. Have you ever thought about the initial nonverbal message you have been sending up until now? Smiling and making direct eye contact with the child is a simple and comfortable way to begin.

Another favorite technique of mine in shifting children out of fearful energy during a procedure is to create confusion by asking them to change chairs or even change rooms if possible. Why? you may ask. Exactly what I'm hoping they will ask themselves. It can beautifully interrupt their current thinking pattern; and the moment you recognize it as interrupted, immediately interject a positive suggestion concerning their experience with you.

An example that made me laugh as to how easily this works was with a ten-year-old boy who wanted to fight his way through getting his blood drawn. The first technician tried and failed to get anywhere in gaining cooperation and asked for my help.

"He won't hold out his arm or help me at all," she said, "and he refuses to try any of my suggestions."

I walked in the room with a relaxed smile and asked, "What's wrong?"

"She's going to poke me with that needle, and it's going to hurt," the boy said.

"Well if you sit over here," I said, pointing to a chair across the room, "you won't feel a thing," as I walked over to the other chair. He looked dazed. Ahh...the turning point! Immediately I reinforced, "You won't feel a thing," as he objected. How could changing chairs possibly have anything to do with it? That moment of temporary confusion was all I needed to stop his current pattern of thinking and redirect it into a positive expectation of how easy it is to get your blood drawn.

I repeated the same positive confident statement over and over, "You won't feel a thing, but you have to sit over here."

He came over to the chair, entirely puzzled, by the look on his face. He let me draw his blood uneventfully. As I asked him to relax his arm, he stared at the needle penetrating his skin.

The point of the patient's confusion is the high point of your creativity. That's where you interject a confident, positive statement that your heart and nonverbal language support as to what you want the child to experience. Correct formulation of your statement is important, of course. "If you sit over here, you won't feel a thing," gets a better response than saying, "If you sit over here it won't hurt." Most injections children receive don't really hurt anyway. It's the *idea* of a long needle penetrating your skin that hurts, not the needle itself. It's psychological pain, not physical; and this is where we can make a huge difference. Many procedures fit into this category. The idea of the procedure is far worse than the event itself.

A Second Chance at a First Approach

Sometimes your initial approach comes after someone else's. The first nurse goes in to do his or her best, meets obstinence, and a battle begins. I have been fortunate in my career to have associated with many nurses who recognize that although the hornet's nest has been initially stirred up, they realize all is not lost and ask for help. Nancy, a coworker of mine in the ER, was one such sensitive individual. She involved me in the process of attempting to salvage the expected outcome of reducing a fractured forearm and applying a cast in a youngster. Nancy informed me that her patient, Terry, was extremely fearful and attempts at gaining her cooperation were unsuccessful. The parents were overprotective, upset about having to wait in the ER as long as they did, and concerned about the seriousness of their daughter's injury. The orthopedist arrived, time was short and Terry was a long way away from a positive experience.

The doctor went to the front desk for the chart and to look at the x-rays. I went straight to the patient's room. When I got there, both parents were obviously upset, their child was visibly frightened and her face was all red from crying. Nine years old, Terry stood in the corner of the room next to her parents. They all shared a similar look of fear and huddled close together as if they were operating from some protective instinct. I began by just slowing things down. I came into the room not wanting anything other than an understanding of how this child and family were perceiving things. In this situation, how you breathe is a powerful nonverbal message. Although everyone in the room had rapid shallow breathing, I maintained slow deep respirations. I walked slowly, talked slowly and shared a calming presence just long enough to gain a hint of rapport. I talked to the parents while they described the mechanism of her injury. As the parents began to realize I wanted nothing but the best experience for their child, they lightened up just enough for their daughter to notice. At that point I turned my attention to the child.

"If I don't touch your arm, will you show it to me?" I asked.

She took a small step forward and revealed her swollen, mildly distorted forearm held in a sling, which she supported with her other hand. Ahh...the turning point! That small step was the most cooperation she had willingly offered anyone. I took it as the only opportunity I had to redirect the fear that was still present and immediately interjected a statement suggesting a positive outcome to shift her expectations. In that moment, I poured my heart into my words.

"The more you relax your whole body, the easier the doctor can help you feel better," I said. A temporary moment of stillness reflected in her eyes as her crying began to subside.

Anticipating the doctor's needs, I positioned the height of the stretcher and arranged the room. I talked about how fortunate they were that this particular physician was on call that day, which gave a refocusing of issues and kept our rapport going. It also served as a welcome distraction.

Continuously, I downplayed the entire procedure by repeating, "All you have to do is relax your whole body like you're asleep." We were making headway, but I needed another step forward in her cooperation.

"Will you at least sit on the stretcher to see if I have it adjusted to the right height for you?" I questioned. The height of the stretcher was irrelevant. I just wanted to build small steps of cooperation and trust, and I had little time to do it.

I made this request while I was arranging supplies, giving her plenty of time to come up with her own decision about whether or not to sit on the stretcher. Had I stood too close, face to face, or used an assertive tone, she would have perceived my request as too insistent. Instead, I was across the room, with my body turned away from her without eye contact. It worked! Through the rapport I had created in our short time together, I managed to persuade her just to sit at first, and then again to lie down. At this point, Terry had responded favorably to several requests for cooperation. However small, we were clearly moving in the right direction.

"Relax your whole body and especially your arm — like it's asleep," I continuously repeated. I asked Nancy to reinforce those same words. Nancy and I both knew that without muscular resistance, manipulating the bone back in place would be much easier for both the patient and the doctor.

The physician entered the room with a reassuring smile, and began explaining the procedure. During his conversation he looked at Terry and said, "All you have to do is relax your arm like it is asleep."

Nancy had asked the doctor, as well, to reinforce the same message we were giving all along. By now, the child had heard that same line so many times from three different people, it wasn't hard for her to know what to do. Through the rapport we established, her level of anxiety decreased enough that she willingly allowed the doctor to hold and support her arm out of the sling without objecting. Although fear was still present in the child, it no longer controlled her. She entered into a state of empowerment. As the doctor manipulated her arm, she did not move or resist him and followed our instructions. Terry hollered out when pressure was applied to reset the bone. The intervention was brief.

"We're done," the doctor said, as she surprisingly looked at him with a tear rolling down her face with a fragile look of relief. "I just need to apply the cast, but the hard part is over now," the doctor said, as her parents filled the room with sighs of relief.

It will take a little more practice to reset the expectations and level of cooperation in instances where you are not the patient's first encounter, but it's important to remember that they haven't met you yet! Your initial approach is different from anyone else's.

What I have learned about these situations is that the doubt exists in you more than in your patients. If you believe you and your patient are at a disadvantage just because you're called in to help when someone else has already failed, then indeed you are. That much more confidence is being asked of you, in regards to your own self-determination to recreate expectations of a positive experience. It is a higher level of responsibility to assign to yourself, but it's also a higher level of success that you get to feel.

Once you discover that the level of success depends more on your commitment than on the patient's level of fear, success will visit you more frequently — even when others have failed.

Most of what makes a good nurse develop into a great nurse is his or her level of personal involvement. Not just with your patients, but simultaneously within yourself. Time and experience build tremendous confidence. Now it all boils down to one thing: whose energy is stronger — the fear and obstinence of the child or your belief in the powerful, confident person you are? You will create a good experience by insisting on one. Let the challenge begin! Changing apprehension into cooperation with your presence and initial approach leaves a powerful feeling of success. That success is shared not only with you, your patients and their families, but also with the doctor, the medical team and the very reputation of the institution itself.

SUMMARY

1) Look back and review the initial approach you have been using with frightened children. Are you getting a level of cooperation that works well for you and your patients? Can you move it to an even higher level through the use of rapport, intention or in creating more favorable expectations?

2) Examine in greater detail the content of the nonverbal messages you have been sending up to now. Have you been aware of them? What single word describes your body language? Are you open and friendly, or do you project some level of fear of the situation yourself? How close do you initially stand to your patients to help them feel more comfortable, and do you make any attempt to be at eye level?

3) Are you in touch with your own ability as a professional and the tremendous impact you can make, or do you feel a victim of circumstances? Are you aware of the thoughts that run through your own mind that influence your action? When all looks lost at gaining cooperation, do you give up too easily or continue to stay persistent with what you believe you can make possible for your patients?

4) Confusion can be used as an opportunity and can be a powerful tool to redirect negative thinking into expectations that are much more positive. Look for ways to create confusion intentionally in order to disrupt a patient's negative thinking pattern. Once interrupted, that's the moment to interject a positive statement and repeat that statement frequently.

5) Are you aware of the subtleties that patients present to you — looks and phrases that constitute what I have described as "the turning point"? Are you recognizing those atomic moments of subtle cooperation as a major opportunity? This can be anything from a small step forward, a slowing down of breathing or an obvious change in their perception of things by the look on their face. Learn to act quickly when you recognize the turning point by interjecting powerful, positive statements spoken with heartfelt confidence, and backed with a sound intention. Use proper semantics.

6) Always breathe slowly and deeply in front of a fearful child.

7) During your initial approach, remember not only to tell the child what's going to happen, but also how they are going to *experience* what happens.

Take a closer look at all the messages you're projecting... Take the time needed to connect with the child and to build at least some degree of rapport.

"Fear is that little darkroom where
negatives are developed."
–Michael Pritchard

7: Use the Energy of Fear to Your Advantage

*O*rdinarily, we tend to conclude that fear in a child is bad, and that we are already placed at a disadvantage when working with children right from the start. Consider the fact that fear is intense, concentrated energy in motion in crude form, a diamond in the rough. Train yourself to immediately look upon it as an abundance of raw fuel at your disposal. Start to perceive the fear itself as a powerful springboard to have the potential to propel the child through the very experience with which they are faced. See the situation as potentially favorable for both of you and begin to consider all the creative avenues the energy of fear can be rechanneled into. Remember from our very first chapter that the energy of fear in children lends itself to being transformational.

Have you ever tried to motivate or influence someone who is just sitting there emotionless, like a lump of clay? Dead and energetically lifeless like the proverbial bump on a log? You feel as if you need a team of wild horses to get something moving in the person. A complete lack of any sign of energy makes it so much harder, so much more challenging, to attempt to provoke change. It seems you have nothing to work with when you're getting little to no response. Fear gives you something to work with. Train your thought process to have this automatic response.

If you can associate the child's fear with opportunity, you have already made an impact on the nature of it, and on the way it's carried and expressed in both of you. As always, it's how we look at a situation, rather than the situation itself, that has the greatest impact on where things are going to go from there. What you reflect back in that moment of fear even in thought form becomes pivotal because that's your starting point. By remaining aware of your own immediate reactions and responses in the presence of this emotion, you set up acceptance rather than aversion within yourself. Now you've created an opening to offer that very same idea to the child. With a little direction and commitment on your part, children will willingly trade in their fear for something better simply to relieve the tension. Energy by its very nature is never static. It has to move. So all we do is give it something of our own design to move into.

Redirecting the Child's Fear

For example, William, a seven-year-old boy, came into the emergency room to have several sutures removed from his forearm. His parents chose not to accompany him, so he walked into the department from the waiting room by himself. He was already trembling, anxious and on the verge of tears as we approached the treatment room. His brown hair was disheveled, and the growing look of fear on his face intensified as he sat up on the stretcher. When we were alone in the room, his anxiety escalated.

"How are you doing?" I asked, standing next to him just trying to look at his forearm. He started screaming and yelling and immediately objected to my presence and instantly covered his already-healed wound with his other hand. He aggressively refused to let me look at it. William shouted out even louder when Beth, my coworker, walked into the room with a "let's get this over with, we're too busy" attitude.

"Just restrain him and take out the sutures," Beth said to me quietly as she left the room.

At this point, he started crying, and anything I said was not heard as he became more and more uncooperative and completely unwilling to communicate. It was almost as if he was inviting us to strap him down and proceed the hardest way possible. Perhaps this expectation was set in place at his initial visit and, therefore, it was a natural conclusion for him to believe that fearful resistance was the only way to behave.

108

I was extremely busy, but held firm in my belief that there was no need to do things the hard way, even though I had little time to convince him otherwise. I never once thought of holding him down and letting him scream to quickly remove his stitches, even though it probably would have been a lot faster, as my coworker had pointed out.

Instead, I stopped talking. I opened the door of the supply cart and placed in his hands a roll of tape and some unsterile gauze.

"Here... make me a bandage," I said, and without waiting for a reply I left the room. Fifteen minutes later, after tending to more urgent needs I returned to his room. He was gone.

I asked Beth where he was and she said, "Oh...we're finished. He was so involved in his bandage-making I just took out his seven stitches while neither one of us said a word!" In and out, just as she had wanted, the easy approach I wanted and a simple distraction the boy eventually came to know he wanted. A win-win-win situation.

"He was too involved in what *he* was doing to pay any attention to what *I* was doing," Beth said.

That was some pretty intense bandage-making, wouldn't you say? It was, in fact, a direct reflection of the same intense energy that had been expressed as fear. William was given the opportunity to rechannel his energy. I wish I had a picture of that complicated tangled mess of a bandage he left on the stretcher. It looked like all his fear, anxiety and agitation were still lying there.

The energy of fear, by its very nature, is based in movement. Don't be in a hurry to decide where the energy is going to land. Instead, begin to explore all the creative ways you can help it find a much more constructive direction.

No matter how long I have been doing this work, I am still surprised at how surprised I get watching fear turn around, when initially it looked like it just wanted to stay rooted. Give it an ounce of patience and enough space to let it surprise you. Time and time again it will. You may not succeed 100 percent of the time, but holding children down, tying them to a papoose board and restraining them will be rare and unnecessary. It would have been an eye-opening experience for William's parents to have witnessed the creative talent their boy demonstrated within himself and his potential to deal with fears as an adult. When the ability to confront fear is reinforced in our children, they too can see the strength and internal resources they have available within themselves, with an ever-increasing awareness. What a valuable skill to have in many of life's experiences to come.

Crystal, a six-year-old child, is another remarkable example. She came into the hospital sobbing. She was crying so loud we could hear her all the way from the ER waiting room. Crystal was in pain, afraid of the medical staff and exhibited chaotic breathing as she took rapid, short inhalations. The waiting room was completely full as she sat between her parents. Her hair was beaded and braided as her little feet dangled from the chair while she continued to cry. I walked out to the waiting room to greet her.

"She has pain in her stomach, but she's more afraid of having to come to the hospital," her father said. "She's been crying like that in the car the whole time coming here," he added. While she was bent over holding her abdomen, I kneeled down in front of her at eye level.

Right in-between her crying breaths, coinciding with an inhale, I interjected, "Would you like me to show you a real easy way to help this?"

Her rapid breathing and crying continued. But then, suddenly, that one simple statement and the intention behind it had a surprising impact. Crystal looked up at me with tears still rolling down her cheeks, as her wet eyes gazed intently into mine. Abruptly, she stopped crying, nodded her head yes and agreed on the spot. It was that easy!

"Come on back with me," I said, as I stood up and held out my hand. The packed waiting room got pretty quiet. All eyes were on her as she got up, took my hand and walked back to the treatment room as one of her parents followed.

Now that her cycle of fear was interrupted I filled our conversation with favorable expectations. Crystal seemed to prefer talking over imagination. I asked a lot of questions and allowed her to do as much talking as possible, repeating back what little she said to me. All of the energy that was sitting there in the form of fear was being funneled into our conversation. Crystal was extremely willing to try an alternative to crying and being afraid. If we look at it from her perspective, it was a welcome relief from all the unpleasant things she was most likely thinking about.

Even though it was painful, Crystal allowed the doctor to palpate and examine her abdomen. She no longer clung to fear even when the physician expressed concern about her medically, ordered an extensive work-up and called in a surgical consult. She permitted me to start an intravenous line without resistance. While getting x-rays and blood work done, she remained calm. Her parents were delighted with the treatment they received. They said we took care of all their daughter's needs, not just her medical condition.

When I look back on this experience, I realize that so much more went into my initial approach with her than just the words, "Would you like me to show you a real easy way to help this?" My experiences have me absolutely convinced it *can* be done that way. Confidence has magic in it. I didn't just say it. I knew it. Personal conviction, I firmly believe, is transmitted in your tone of voice, in your eyes, the way you walk and the words you choose. It dictates the expressions on your face and the type of energy that emanates from you. It's as if it flows out of you and onto the child in some indescribable way — a way that children respond to.

Participating in a child's good experience becomes something of a personal addiction, a high you'll want to experience over and over again. Multiple experiences of success will build your confidence level, and you'll become more comfortable facing unique challenges.

Redirecting Your Own Fear

Martial artists are well known for capitalizing on the raw energy of fear as a powerful fuel source. When confronted with a bigger, stronger, more challenging opponent, the approaching fear is used as only a signal, a trigger, to tap into memories and experiences in their life when they *were* powerful and in control. Moments when they felt, thought and acted determined and invincible suddenly become the focus. For these experts, fear is only the driving force to enter into a heightened state. Described as similar to a slingshot effect, the energy of fear is stretched to a certain point and then suddenly released in an unexpected, beneficial direction. They actually learn to use the fear to make themselves more formidable.

Begin to explore this idea when the situation presents itself by immediately looking into the fear and considering where the available energy can be directed. How might your facial expressions change when you fully engage the possibility? How might your eyes deliver the message now that you're convinced it's possible? The possibilities you perceive may actually be reflected back onto the child. Give them the chance to copy your calm confidence and use your initial approach to its greatest advantage.

This entire concept is so much easier to understand when you have experienced the energy of fear take on a new direction within yourself. My own experience happened at Camp Coqui, a diabetes camp for kids that I participate in every summer. The children practice a variety of team-building skills including a ropes course. Part of this course includes an exercise called the pamper pole. While tethered, you climb a phone poll, stand on top of it without anything to hold onto, then jump off to try and catch a swinging trapeze. I was afraid of falling backwards, so I avoided the exercise and the uncomfortable way it made me feel. Since I prefer to be an example of the things I teach, it became harder and harder to ignore my own fear. I could no longer pretend it didn't exist and that I didn't have to face it. Because of this, I finally had to accept the challenge.

Just because you work with and teach children doesn't mean you're not the one doing the learning. Children are the most profound and subtle teachers one can find. It's easy to miss this if you're too immersed in your own adult ego. Then it's embarrassing to learn from children because you're supposed to be older, wiser and smarter. But we can no longer remain divided when our intention has led us to being on equal ground. A secure adult is invariably willing to learn from any experience, in any environment, in any form the teacher may take.

So I had to climb the pole! Slowly and deliberately I climbed all the way up to the last rung. I held my balance as I managed to stand on top of the pole without anything to hold onto. The greatest part of this experience for me was that I did it without the slightest increase in heart rate or breathing as the pole wobbled beneath my feet. All of my fear and apprehension moved into concentration and a rather elated feeling of accomplishment and empowerment. In that moment, I could easily relate to how the kids feel when they overcome their own challenges in the hospital.

In our personal lives as adults, we can create an escape by rationalizing our way out of confronting fear. Kids in the hospital don't have that option. There's no back door to escape from. This is the greatest reason the energy of fear is compelled to move forward.

Having personal experience in seeing fear shift within yourself makes it easier to impart that understanding and ability in someone else. Where in your life have you experienced something similar? Bring that understanding to the forefront when you're with kids who think fear is stronger than anything else they possess inside them.

Distracting Fear

"Can you take a look at my patient?" Mike, a coworker of mine, asked. "I'm not sure how to best help him. He sustained multiple fractures, and he's writhing on the stretcher. He already received IV pain medicine."

Entering the room, I saw a young man lying on the stretcher, rocking back and forth and crying out in pain. Sweat rolled down his face, which was red from grimacing. The first thing that grabbed my attention was his loud, rapid, shallow breathing. He was hyperventilating.

"Breathe here," I commanded, placing the palm of my hand on his abdomen just below his belly button so he could feel it. His breathing changed slightly, probably because I helped him become more aware of how chaotic it was.

I took one loud, prolonged exhale so he could hear it and repeated, "Breathe from your belly." He stopped rolling back and forth long enough to make an attempt to follow my instructions. Mike and I supported his efforts. Gradually he was able to shift all the energy he was expending into his breath, taking it as deeply as possible into his abdomen. Pain medication helps to relieve pain, but it can have very little effect on fear. Together, we helped him refocus his attention long enough to allow the analgesics to take a deeper effect. All he needed was that temporary distraction to accomplish that. Sometimes these brief, seemingly minor interventions mean a great deal to our patients.

The most dramatic example I've ever witnessed of distracting fear involved a patient who came by ambulance to the ER. He was taken straight to the trauma room where critical patients who need immediate intervention are placed. The room is bigger to accommodate a medical team and portable equipment. Since he was my assigned patient, I was at the head of the bed surrounded by the interventional team. The patient was tachycardic, diaphoretic and his breathing was rapid and shallow. His blood pressure was elevated and he showed signs of physical and emotional distress. His body was in a state of total muscular rigidity, and all I saw were the whites of his eyes when I attempted to examine his pupils. He was barely responsive. Intravenous lines were already in place as Doctor Hamilton began his examination and assessment.

After several minutes, I heard the patient mumble, "I'm dying, I'm dying."

"What's wrong?" I questioned further. He arrived alone, we had very little information on his medical history and this was his first verbal interaction with anyone.

"I'm dying," he repeated, as he continued to writhe on the stretcher.

"From what?" I questioned.

"My family told me I'm going to die from my heart condition," he muttered.

After a few more questions, I shared my assessment of him with Doctor Hamilton. I believed he was having a full-blown anxiety attack, as dramatic as he presented. Most of the team members had a look of disbelief on their faces that anxiety alone was responsible for his immediate condition. He appeared acutely ill either metabolically or neurologically. The doctor ordered preliminary studies and asked me to stay by his side and talk with him. The interventional team dispersed, staying on standby, as I remained alone in the room with him. I was able to talk him down slowly, using a soft tone of voice and remaining as calm as I could, given my own shot of adrenaline. Gradually, his fear, tachycardia, hypertension, muscular rigidity and other associated symptoms began to settle as I distracted him with calming conversation, reassuring him he was in no immediate danger. He did have a heart condition, we came to find out, but it was minor and completely stable. His family indulged him in negative, fearful conversation that scared him. Unfortunately, he funneled his fear into more fear, which precipitated an anxiety attack the likes of which none of us had ever seen before. Once I realized how he was mismanaging his fear, I was able to redirect it into calming conversation, which acted as a simple diversion. All of his test results came back within normal limits. After a few hours of observation he was discharged.

My most amusing experience was when I talked a young man into approaching his fear of a procedure from an unusual angle. Together, we agreed that when the doctor entered the room and began his procedure, he would immediately close his eyes, relax his entire body and take himself mentally to the beach and stay there until I gave him a cue. I didn't say anything to the doctor about the patient's serious apprehensions and we were all pretty quiet the whole time. The procedure took about fifteen minutes. Despite his fear, the boy remained absolutely silent and unmoving while distracted by his mental imagery.

When it was all over, the doctor looked at me and asked, "Was I that good?" — presumptuously assigning all the credit to himself!

Overwhelm the Fear

Occasionally, I don't even need to assess where the child is at in relation to fear, how they perceive the situation at hand, or what obstacles confront them. At times it's irrelevant what they bring to the table when they are overtaken, overwhelmed and flooded with an energy that feels convinced, and a heart that knows wherever they are, the best possible experience is waiting for them. Enthusiasm, desire, conviction, confidence, intention and love all gang up on them to the point they couldn't possibly want to settle in fear. Repeatedly, children have handed over their trust and laid it right in my lap when offered alternatives. Now, that's what I call a papoose board! Tied up and immobilized by this crazy nurse with a dedicated vision of working with children "the easy way." Give them a chance to surprise you with their innocence.

A businessman was in a hurry packing for his trip while his three-year-old daughter was having a wonderful time playing on the bed.

115

At one point she said, "Daddy look at this," and stuck out two of her fingers.

Trying to keep her entertained, he reached out and stuck her tiny fingers in his mouth and said, "Daddy's gonna eat your fingers!" pretending to gobble them up before he rushed out of the room again.

When he returned, his daughter was standing on the bed staring at her fingers with a devastated look on her face.

"What's wrong, honey? he asked.

"What happened to my booger?" she replied.

Fear Transformed Touches Many Lives

Even those who participate on a peripheral level benefit in some way. Like the parents, for example, watching them swell with pride as they observe their child overcome a situation previously viewed as fearful.

Parents will say to their children, "I can't believe how brave you were!" (I hear that one a lot), or "You were amazing." And of course every father's favorite, "You were such a trooper." I love to hear a brother or sister say, "I wish I had stitches," when they see the sucker in the mouth when it's over and all the attention their sibling just received. It makes us question as adults how well we handle our own challenges and fears. Perhaps it makes us believe we can be better ourselves.

Share Your Ideas and Skills with Physicians

Doctor Richard L. Harrison, medical director of HealthSouth Larkin Hospital in Miami, Florida, shared an experience he had. In his letter to me dated June 17, 1995, he wrote:

> *A young man dislocated his shoulder. An experienced emergency physician had been trying to reduce it, but had been unsuccessful despite the use of parenteral analgesics, sedatives and muscle relaxants. When I saw the patient he was awake, alert and beginning to complain of the return of pain. I used*

the distraction and relaxation methods you and I discussed. I consider them similar to some meditative techniques. When the patient is receptive, the relaxation is achieved in minutes, and that is how long it took to reduce this patient's shoulder.

I was fortunate to work with Dr. Harrison, who encouraged my work, took a personal interest in it himself and became my friend.

I don't believe we need a double-blind placebo-based study to understand how transforming fear works. It's not science — it's love. To attempt to study an intangible quality like love implies an inability to approach things through your heart, through your own love, and drink from the mystery of its blessing. Don't study it, do it! And why are we not teaching love in medicine? How else are we to really heal if not through each other?

SUMMARY

1) Understand that the fear children express is not always as it appears to be.

2) Learn to respond, not react, the moment you see a fearful child. Train yourself to use the energy of fear as your raw fuel source to transform that fear into more favorable responses from children. Know in your heart the energy we label as fear can be creatively redirected into imagination, conversation and rapport.

3) Greet fear with a loving intention.

4) Realize how willing children are to allow their fear to be distracted. Children prefer to relieve the tension of fear and crying through more creative outlets, when given the opportunity.

5) Practice shifting fear within yourself. When you experience a shift of fear in yourself, it's easier to envision it in the children with whom you work.

*Just because you work with
and teach children doesn't
mean you're not the one doing
the learning.*

―•―⋈◊⋈―•―

"Beware lest you lose the substance
by grasping at the shadow."
–Aesop

―•―⋈◊⋈―•―

8: See the Phantom in the Phobia

*O*f all the dramatic phobias I have met over the years, this story is one of my favorites. An endocrinologist asked me to work with a twelve-year-old and his parents to help the boy learn how to use an insulin pump instead of taking four to five insulin shots a day. He had type 1 diabetes for ten years, as he had been diagnosed at the age of two. The boy was smart, and his parents were attentive, involved and supportive. We started at 9:30 A.M., and I had an initial two-hour appointment to teach the technology of the device and the associated skills. Most of that time is spent in reviewing the pump screens, scrolling down to the right function and entering data. A small, flexible catheter is placed under the skin and remains there for three days. Most patients find this much better than so many injections on a daily basis. It's like one injection every three days instead of a total of twelve, so it's a welcome change in that respect.

The teaching progressed very well, and the boy and both his parents picked up on everything pretty quickly. Then it came time to insert the small catheter under his skin. I handed the loaded device to the boy and instructed him on how it automatically inserts the catheter for him by holding it up against his skin and pushing a little button. Reluctantly, he held it in his hands and just looked at me a little longer than necessary as I sensed something wasn't right.

"I can't do this," he said as he handed it back to me.

"Yes, you can," I replied and went to touch his abdomen to show him where, with the device still lying on the table. He shoved my hand away, backed up his chair and started hyperventilating. The color dropped out of his face as he turned white, and for a minute, I thought he was going to faint and hit the floor. I don't carry smelling salts in my office like some of my coworkers, but I was beginning to think that now would have been a good time to start! He started to perspire. The look on his face was like I had just cornered a hunted animal and was moving in for the kill.

"He's never given a shot to himself before," his father announced. "We've been giving them to him."

He had been diagnosed at the age of two with diabetes, and this twelve-year-old boy had never learned self-injection skills. His parents had been doing it for him for the past ten years. I wasn't informed about that part! I looked down at my watch and it was 11:15. There were fifteen minutes left to our appointment. By 11:35 this boy broke through his fear for the first time in ten years and gave himself his very first injection. Here's how it happened.

"What if today was the day you were no longer afraid?" I asked, as I looked into his eyes giving him a moment to collect himself. I received no response other than a fixated stare from a still-pale face and an immobilized body.

"Can you imagine what your life would be like if being afraid wasn't a part of your life anymore?" I continued. His eyes moved upward as he tried to access even in imagination what that would be like. He didn't answer that question either but probably for the first time in his life he thought about it. He nervously stood up in my crowded little office space and narrowly paced the floor. His parents silently witnessed our exchange.

"Let's make today that day," I said as I picked up the still-ready device and placed it back in his hands. Again, he took it with reluctance but this time he held it without immediately putting it back down as I watched his thoughts and emotions continue to whirl. He stood next to me for a moment as we again looked into each other, and then he sat back down still holding onto the device but with a totally defeated body posture.

"You can do this," I said, "and you're going to laugh at how easy it is. You're going to wonder why this whole thing ever bothered you in the first place."

It's never the words alone people respond to, it's *you* they respond to. He knew that I knew he could overcome his phobic behavior to the point he at least started to think about believing it himself. We played with that little device for the remaining ten minutes. He put it on his skin, off his skin, in his hands, back on the table and then back in his hands again. His parents encouraged him, as did I, as he once again held it to his skin but just couldn't get himself to push the button. By now he was trembling and sweating profusely.

"You push it," he said, as he turned to his parents. I nixed the idea.

"This is part of learning pump therapy and it has to come from you," I said. I promised I wouldn't touch him and moved in physically closer to support his efforts. He trusted me and allowed my close proximity, but then he stood up and paced some more, and I let him. It was getting late. Not really though, because I could have missed lunch and belabored it further, but I didn't.

Finally, I picked up his insulin pump and with a defeated tone I stood up and said, "Maybe this isn't for you. Maybe you're just not ready." He didn't like that and neither did his parents. I behaved as if I was immediately ending the session. "I'll let your doctor know," I said. They all knew I meant it. Actually though, it was a complete bluff. It was my final push to end the stalemate.

"No," he said, with a surprisingly determined tone. He paused a moment or two longer, held the device to his abdomen and pushed the button.

"Did you even feel that?" I immediately asked him.

"No, I didn't!" he exclaimed, as a thousand volts of energy released by his shattered fear rushed to fill the void in his now-exuberant face. The shift in the feeling of my little office space was dramatically obvious as all together we rejoiced.

Still wet from perspiring, he came over to stand next to me. Beaming with a smile and with a glow in his eyes he said, "I'm so glad you're my educator."

In that moment, it was truly I who felt the honor to have him as my patient as we slapped a silly handshake. I know how hard he had to battle with himself and how hard I had to roll up my sleeves and do battle with him. Ten years of phobic fear found itself condensed and cornered in those last twenty minutes. Everything I said, everything I did, everything I believed came from seeing him capable of releasing his fears. Don't pay too much attention to the patient's resistance. Just remember to stay focused on your vision. Patience, persistence and a relentless belief in your patient's abilities create the best environment to break through the fear we label as phobia.

Now that he had found his power, the boy started spouting off assertive statements of independence while looking at his parents and even boasted something about "moving away." He rattled on for a moment or two about some other things he believed he could do now in the typical annoying fashion only teenagers can do. Now it was our turn to just be silent, sit still and listen.

I saw him and his family a second time and, although he wasn't instantaneously free of all his fears, he was on his way. The excitement was toned down and he started his new life on an insulin pump.

Belonephobia

The type of phobia we have been discussing so far with many of these children is called belonephobia, the fear of needles or sharp-pointed objects. As you have seen by now, this type of fear is really no different from any other kind of fear, and it's just as willing to release itself and be transformed. Many of the texts refer to it as a morbid fear. Morbid comes from the Latin root *mordidus* meaning sick or pertaining to disease. I find the secondary definition in all my years of experience much more accurate — a preoccupation with unwholesome ideas or circumstances. They become fixated on anticipating the worst. By this very definition, applying the law of expectations and changing what the child anticipates and expects to happen out of their interactions with you, becomes your most powerful tool for working children through a successful process.

As easily as belonephobic fears are born, they can just as easily be laid to rest. Phobic fear is not stronger or superior to other fears. It's a learned behavior, and with the ideas, approaches and suggestions you have been given so far, you can easily teach children a much better response.

Key Considerations in Helping Children Break through Needle Phobia

1) It always starts with you and your style of approach. Your attitudes and beliefs will influence all your words and actions. Phobic fear is not any

more resistant to releasing itself than any other kind of fear. By believing in the power fear has over children who are afraid of needles, you're believing in the same thing everyone else does, and you're going to get the same results everyone else does too. So the first thing is to clearly recognize your feelings with what it means to you to work with belonephobics. All the approaches and suggestions you have learned thus far equally apply to this type of fear. My best advice is to lead through example. Become fearless yourself and allow their fear to patiently sit in your presence.

2) Choose your words carefully by using refined semantics. On a separate sheet of paper, try this exercise. Write down what you would say and the exact words you would use for the following situations. Take time with your phrases so you get comfortable with your verbal reply. Remember to choose words that diffuse or downplay the whole idea of what people believe about themselves and the power fear has over those with needle phobias.

   a. You're about to give an injection to an extremely anxious individual who is very fearful of needles, and they back up when they see you coming...

   b. A child you're assigned to starts to cry the minute you walk into the room with a syringe in your hand...

   c. You're just about to start a large bore intravenous catheter and the patient says, "I'm scared to death of needles," and pulls his arm away from you...

   d. A patient looks you in the eye and says, "I always faint when my blood is drawn," just as you're about to draw his blood...

Now that you have had a chance to come up with your own suggestions, review the following statements that have worked so well for me in my own practice:

"Would you like to learn an easy way to have this done?"
"I'll show you how to take a shot and you won't even feel it."
"You won't believe how easy this is."

"People leave here all the time feeling great because they're not afraid anymore."

"It's no big deal. Let me show you how to relax your arm like it's asleep."

"You're going to laugh at how easy this is. Let me show you how."

"I know a way you can take a shot and laugh at the same time."

"By the time we're done, you'll be showing other people how to do this as well."

Note: These words are spoken with powerful confidence because you're so convinced yourself. You're not just repeating phrases, you're going to back up your statements and show them how. Remember, it's always the quality of the dedication and the vision you carry that your patients respond to, not the words alone.

3) Immediately apply the law of expectations, as it is your most powerful tool for success. From the very beginning, continuously insist on the ease with which you can help the child comfortably experience injections or any procedures involving needles. The tone of all of your conversation for the rest of your encounter comes from this standpoint. You're setting the expectation that in front of you, they will express themselves quite differently from what they may have been used to. Notice how the above-suggested statements are the exact opposite of what most children or adults presume about phobic fear: It's not easy, it's difficult. You don't laugh, that's ridiculous, you cry. Of course I will feel it and it has to hurt, that's why I'm afraid in the first place! It is this very thought process that needs your help to find balance.

4) Support all your statements with action. Show patients how to intentionally remove tension from their extremities using your own relaxed arm as an example. Actively encourage them to engage their imagination using positive visual pictures for them to focus on. Shift their attention to abdominal breathing and breathe along with them. Take advantage of the rapport you have created by persisting in the actions you'll need to take together to make their favorable experience happen. Give them continuous positive feedback by reinforcing each small step they take forward

along the way. Teach them how not to be afraid of the fear itself by your own example and by communicating to them that feeling it is only a natural part of the process. As a team, use the energy of the child's fear to build the momentum to break through the very situation they're facing.

5) Have a clear and dedicated vision with focus. You will notice how your vision becomes stronger and stronger with each successful interaction, which builds more and more confidence. Eventually you'll begin to view yourself as a powerful resource to teach your patients the art of the dissolution of fear, phobic or otherwise. Combine all of the skills we have discussed so far, especially the ones you're attracted to or that come naturally to you.

6) Practice patience and persistence. Never give up, even if your patients do. From your perspective, you're always ready and available on a moment's notice. You never lose track of their positive possibilities because you know children will often hold out until the very last moment to find their breakthrough. Self-empowerment never comes late. It's always right on time.

7) It's all in your attitude. It's all in how you talk and the words you use and the vision you carry that become believable to those you work with. Because you're so powerfully convinced yourself, you spread confidence. Be contagious. Once you see the jump from phobic to empowered, you'll understand it's more than just the writing and the ideas presented here. It's in you and in your passion and vision and the manner in which you bring that to the child.

The reason I have been so personally successful in removing phobias is because I don't believe in them. That's not what I see when I'm faced with a frightened phobic child. The phobia doesn't exist for me. I see a smart, highly capable, creative child. Develop the vision to see through the phantom presented and into the gifts of empowerment each child carries within. When you do, you remove all of a phobia's presumed power and assumed significance. This, of course, must be done within you first before you can see that same possibility within the child. And, as you undoubtedly believe in the children you work with, only then do they start to believe in themselves.

Children as Teachers

I learned the powerful effect of using proper semantics in working with phobic fear from Hannah, a four-year-old. She taught me a valuable lesson in the power of the correct use of words. Hannah's fear was exaggerated as she bitterly fought with the nursing staff when it came time for injections. I was no exception as I entered her room. When she saw the syringe, she greeted me with ear-piercing screams and struggled in her mother's arms to get away from me. I continued teaching her parents without reacting. I did respond, however, by making eye contact.

As soon as her wet eyes met mine, I emphatically said, "This is so easy, you're going to laugh when you get your medicine." I knew my statement entered her deeply because her breath and her crying paused for a moment. The rhythm was interrupted. Her eyes cautiously remained locked to mine just long enough for her to decide if I really meant what I said; then her crying continued. Her father had to hold her before the injection could be given. The next day, her father told me Hannah worked with the child life specialist who play-acted with a doll. Hannah now had the chance to do to the doll what the nursing staff had needed to do to her. Hannah told the doll she was going to give her a shot and that she would *laugh* when she gave it to her! Hannah's fears were subsiding. She graduated to telling the staff where on her arm she would agree to take the injection and experienced a major breakthrough in her fear. I learned a valuable lesson in just how closely children hear your words, especially in the face of highly charged emotions. Choose them wisely and express them with sincerity.

On the other hand, the most amusing eight-year-old child I ever met was a boy by the name of Clint. I was at the nurses' station reviewing his medical record when I heard a buzz come from the call station and a staff member engaged his intercom.

"May I help you?"

Hannah, Age 4

"Yes, excuse me, but it's twelve o'clock and it's time for my insulin shot please!"

I had to laugh. I never heard that one before. Clint and I had a great time getting to know each other, and he obviously fit into the exact opposite category of a phobic. He was fearlessly self-empowered and literally called all the shots!

Expand the Comfort Zones

In my career, I have seen many overprotective parents unnecessarily perpetuate phobic behavior for years. Sometimes the overprotectiveness of the parents is a far more powerful barrier to overcome than the phobia itself. Each situation needs its own individual evaluation, of course, but predominately it's far more compassionate to help the child through the phobia at a young age rather than miss the opportunity a hospital environment provides and then allow the fear to become ingrained. Often, children are prepared to release their phobia far more quickly than the parents will allow them to. I have seen many times when the actions and imposed beliefs of the parents end up protecting and preserving the phobia itself rather than the well-being of the child.

As a parent myself, I know the territory. You don't want to force an issue on a child who's just not ready, traumatize them and make the situation worse. You also have to realize the remarkable ability children have to reframe their thinking and engage their trust. It's a fine line to step up to and find balance. That's why my insistence is on a gentle, loving but firm approach backed with an intention with vision. Don't be a short-sighted parent and cheat your child out of an opportunity they would ultimately be willing to face. In my thirty years of nursing, I have never met a child who regretted releasing and surrendering their fears or phobias, even if there was some degree of discomfort in getting there. The trade-off is far too substantial. I'm not suggesting a standardized approach that all children must universally apply to. An individualized assessment taking into account each child's specific and unique needs is always part of the process. Being a phobia buster, however, also means you're willing to step out on the skinny branches, take risks and push the comfort zones.

Clint, Age 8

Don't think it's possible any other way; if it were, then it wouldn't be called a phobia.

It has been my experience that a phobia doesn't carry as much energy and unremitting fear as you might think. Many are those who encounter it and allow themselves to be drawn into it and assist in the creation of an energetic feedback loop of approval. Over time, hundreds of people may have confirmed and agreed to its power, reinforcing it. Now, you become the one to stand up to it and pull the plug on its self-perpetuation. Take a stand on the patient's behalf and refuse to acknowledge that the phobia's power is greater than your combined intrinsic resources. Refuse to feed it. Starve it right from the very beginning. From your immediate encounter with it, tirelessly point to a better response — to a transformed, reframed state of empowerment whose primary and secondary gains are going to outweigh anything a crippled, phobic mindset could ever imagine. Consciously, your thoughts, beliefs, reactions and emotional responses steamroller right over the top of how powerful a phobia believes itself to be. You don't and won't buy it. No matter what happens, remain insistent that the phobia is easy to release and an unnecessary, outdated expression. There are hundreds of other options that are far more empowering. Deep inside you laugh in the face of its energy, because you know it's claiming to be the master when it's even less than a servant. You see through it for what it really is: incapable of maintaining itself because it's too fragile compared to the powerful resources you and your patient carry within. With your help, you'll reintroduce your patients back to those resources. The ones they have simply forgotten are there.

Powerful talk, I know, but if you back down or flinch in these standpoints, beware. However subtle, you're feeding and taking part in an energy that's begging for a different expression no matter how it's disguised. It's not by chance you're sitting next to it. It was drawn to you, and now you are called to action.

Perhaps now is the time to believe wholeheartedly in yourself. You are a powerful force to reckon with and can dismantle a phobia, or whatever they want to call this fear, as professionally as the best of them.

From what I have seen over the years spending a lot of time and keeping a great deal of company with belonephobias, they're really quite fragile. They are awkward expressions screaming for resolution like an innocent, boisterous child clambering for attention. Like a recurrent nightmare that desperately wants to reveal its contents for what it truly is and be understood, released, resolved and forgotten. Fears and phobias want to come full circle to completion even though it rarely looks that way upon first appearance. Don't be fooled. Believe in a child's inner resources and in the power of the sincere expression of your own.

SUMMARY

1) Reread Chapters 1 and 2.

2) Practice the law of expectations in as many situations as you can until you become comfortable with its use and how it is expressed through you.

3) Review the section on key considerations in this chapter. Practice them independently and then slowly integrate each recommendation into one complete whole.

4) Learn from every child, what he or she has to teach you. They are, in fact, your greatest teachers.

5) Believe in the gentle ease of expanding your own comfort zones so that you can impart that gift to others.

6) Comfort comes with confidence. Practice well so your confidence is earned.

Take a stand on the patient's behalf and refuse to acknowledge that the phobia's power is greater than your combined intrinsic resources.

"The quieter you become,
the more you can hear."
–Ram Dass

9: Use Nonverbal Communication

*M*uch has been written on the communications we deliver without speech. Libraries are full of material, particularly on gestures and the meanings they convey, which vary dramatically from one culture to the next. I was surprised to read in Desmond Morris's book *Body Talk: The Meaning of Human Gestures* that a Thai cabaret singer shot a man because during the performance he crossed his leg, showed the sole of his shoe and pointed it toward the stage performer. This happened in Thailand, and was viewed as the most profound insult a person could deliver, signifying "You are less than the dirt I step on with my shoe and the lowest form of life possible." For Americans, it might be easier to compare this to someone being physically harmed because an obscene hand gesture was given in a heated traffic situation.

My purpose in mentioning these things is to point out how powerfully nonverbal language speaks, and perhaps at times even louder than words themselves. The following outline is not meant to be all-inclusive, but a user-friendly snapshot of the more positive responses I have generally received by using nonverbal messages wisely and with full awareness in a medical setting. By keeping them simple, in this context, we remain natural. In remaining natural, that too becomes a nonverbal message we send as someone who is relaxed and at ease with themself.

Have a Clear Intention

Intention is the strongest nonverbal message we deliver. It drives all of the other nonverbal messages we send and is the foundation for all that follows, including conscious and subconscious mannerisms. It's important you remain very clear on this. It's a lot harder to disguise your true intentions through nonverbal communication than it is with words. You can say one thing and mean another and get away with that to some extent, but not so with your body language. It will give you away.

An example of how easily this blends into our daily lives can be seen through an interaction that occurred when I went for a haircut. I was working on this very chapter at the time. As I walked through the door of the salon, the stylist immediately noticed that I shaved off my beard. Her greeting was as pleasant as always, but it didn't carry her usual warmth. She was looking directly at me, but it was difficult to say what she was actually seeing. She then proceeded to tell me a story about the time her husband shaved off his beard, how upset that made her, and how she acted toward him because of it.

"He didn't look like a mountain man to me anymore," she said. "I told him, 'Don't you ever shave off your beard again' and, by golly, he didn't either," she continued.

As I sat down in the chair, everything felt different. First, the plastic cover to catch the hair was fastened around my neck a notch too tight as if subliminally she was choking the thought of her husband. Our conversation moved elsewhere, but her mannerisms remained abrupt.

She accidentally poked the point of her scissors into my head as if to say "Don't you get the point?" I don't believe she was aware of what she was doing because she offered no apology. Even though she didn't do it that hard, it was obvious. Then, she did the same thing three times with the end of the comb, knocking on my head as if to say, "Hello... anybody home? Don't you know we don't like shaved beards?" Apparently she didn't notice that either! She spun the chair quickly and bumped into my right shoulder and then again on the left as she moved from one side to the other. I never received such a subtle beating in a barber's chair in my life! My daughter laughed at how lopsided my sideburns were left.

All of this was completely unconscious on her part, and had I mentioned it to her she wouldn't have understood what I was talking about. She wasn't doing it intentionally. Exactly my point. She was not clear with her intentions.

The absence of my beard brought up for her thoughts, emotions and memories that expressed themselves through her physical mannerisms. She was not in the moment, she was somewhere else. It showed up in everything she did for those twenty minutes in ways I had never experienced in my ten years as her client.

It would have been fun to see what changes might have occurred if I said, "Stop everything. Let's pretend my beard is still on... or pretend your husband never shaved his off... or pretend I'm not your husband!"

Your intentions don't have to be perfect, just clear. When you act out of unconsciousness, you can't see that you're doing anything unreasonable to the other person at all. Your sensitivity is blunted, and even if it's brought to your attention you're at a loss to comprehend it. Your first tendency, most likely, would be to blame the other person for being too picky, or too sensitive. Chances are you would completely miss the point.

Be present. Stay in the moment with where you are and with what you're doing. When you do so, your intentions will unfold naturally, and you don't even have to think about what you would like to see happen out of your exchange with the other person.

Children are highly tuned into this subtlety and may base their willingness to cooperate solely on their intuitive evaluation of your intentions. Just being there for them is enough. You are not there to impress anyone else, especially yourself. You're there to simply enjoy your work, and your own personal ability to make a difference in the life of a frightened child by keeping their needs in the forefront. Intention is like home plate in baseball. It's the center of the activity and where everything all adds up when it's said and done. *Reread the earlier chapter on Intention.*

Create Calm with Body Posture/Gestures

For kids, gestures are fun and usually associated with exaggerated or animated behavior. A surprised look, like both your hands on top of your head with your mouth wide open or a skip in your walk, often produces a smile. Adults don't usually do that, and you look funny acting that way, especially in a hospital where everyone is so serious.

My favorite part in the movie *Patch Adams* was when he was walking around with metal bedpans for shoes in an open pediatric ward, and the sick kids were howling. I haven't gone that far, but gestures can tickle our funny bone quite easily. Don't be afraid to get creative, if this comes naturally to you. If not, there are plenty of other options to playfully express yourself and have fun — like acting out of character!

Perhaps the area I have experimented with the most is with hand gestures. I have used them successfully to direct children where to physically move in the room while keeping them calm. I want them to move on their own, under their own free will. I don't want to have to pick them up and move them myself. Really, try to avoid that as a last resort. It takes their power away, and our intention is to empower them in a situation where they already feel helpless. Empowering a child just to find the courage to physically move in the needed direction on their own is a powerful first step.

Do not underestimate the power of gesturing and its potential effect. The animal kingdom uses body posture predominately to communicate their intentions with each other or to indicate their hierarchy. Battles are won and lost over how they physically position themselves in relation to each other. Wolves are known to do this almost exclusively. The most common example is an animal rolling over and exposing the vulnerability of the abdominal area as a sign of submission.

I actually taught our dog, Biltmore, to respond to nonverbal commands using only hand gestures. Just by pointing directly at him when we faced each other, he came to understand this meant sit, in order to get his treat. Lowering my hand palm-down made him lie down, palm facing him meant stay, and circular hand motions were his cue to roll over. I'm sure if I took the time with him, together we could have developed quite an extensive nonverbal vocabulary.

People themselves are equally attuned, consciously or subconsciously, to body posture and gestures, and children (who are not in a position of dominance) even more so. Pointing at a child is easily interpreted unconsciously as aggressive. How do you feel when someone points at you if the conversation is controversial? It can often feel blaming or authoritative. Even pointing to an inanimate object like a chair is a nonverbal command to "Sit here." There may be times you want a more authoritative approach if you feel the situation warrants it. Try using tapping gestures instead. Palm-down tapping on the chair or stretcher without looking directly in the child's eyes is a softer version and less intimidating to the kids. The other option I have used successfully is what I call "The Invitation": palm-up, hand slightly cupped, while motioning in the direction they need to be. Usually when your hand is out palm-up, somebody is going to give you something. In this case, it's a subtle gesture suggesting cooperation. Anything they agree to do for you adds up. Salesmen say if they can get you to agree with them by saying yes seven times about anything, then their ability to make the sale is substantially increased. We're actually doing the very same thing. We're selling a concept or an idea that their experience can be made to be comfortable, even if it happens to be an emergency in a hospital.

The main thing with body posture is that you stay in an open-body position. This means nothing crossed, even the legs when sitting. This open posture says, "I am open and available to you." Arms folded across your chest is the most obvious form of protective body language and has little use with kids in a medical context unless it's just for fun.

Your physical distance from children can vary. Adults, however, have more firm distance boundaries and can easily feel their personal space is violated if you stand too close to them.

My brother, Tom, shares the story of an experiment he witnessed where one person intentionally stood just a little too close to another during a normal conversation. Although the distance was slight, it was sufficient to make the other man uncomfortable enough to take a step back. The man doing the experiment gradually stepped closer again and the other man stepped back again. This went on until they ended up all the way down the other end of the hall before the man realized what was happening. Try the military exercise as an experiment where you get a nose-length away from someone's face and then check their comfort level. That posture is intentionally designed to intimidate and create authority in adults.

Children can be sensitive to distance, both standing and sitting, but in my experience they are more forgiving with it than adults. It depends on the child and the circumstances. For example, I recall an emergency room experience I had with a seven-year-old boy named Tom. He was frightened and not sure about how his orthopedic experience was going to turn out. I brought him back to the room so I had a chance to get a feel for him. When it came time to prepare him for his procedure, I bounced into the room, waved hello and sat right next to where he was sitting on the stretcher, giving him a big smile. I deliberately came right into his space. Also, the plane of my body was facing the same way as his, subtly indicating we were both going in the same direction. He was taken by surprise and just sat there and looked at me. I told him exactly how he was going to experience the day with me by his side. I found that with this boy, that close physical distance actually accelerated our bond together, because he and I immediately connected. Remember how fast rapport can happen with kids, so begin to notice what distance feels comfortable for you and the children with whom you work.

On the other hand, I've noticed that when I first walk into the room of younger, frightened children, they can be more sensitive to distance. Especially if my pace is too fast and I stand too close too soon, I'll get a negative response. This seems to be particularly so with children younger than three or four years old. Walking in a slow and calm manner, as simple as that sounds, can make a difference in their reaction and their level of receptivity. Each situation is independent of one another and requires your ability to see into the needs of each particular child. Having fun playing an occasional game of peek-a-boo with frightened toddlers, in appropriate situations, can help break the ice for both parent and child, and can buffer your presence.

The amount of physical tension you feel is most often represented in how you carry yourself, literally carrying the tension right into the room. It becomes more tangible and more visible in someone who is uncomfortable dealing with a child in fear. Your body is a powerful vehicle. Apprehension on your part will show up as fidgety, distant, and uncertain, leading the patient to believe on a subconscious level they have more to be afraid of than they thought. "My nurse is tense because of me," will become a natural conclusion for children to make.

If you have a tendency to carry more physical tension than you would like, take a moment to visualize it dropping from you before you enter the room.

One adult patient I was working with to help relax, shared how he imagined tension leaving his body.

"I am climbing out of a suit of armor," he said with a tone of relief.

It's important that you identify and use a mental image that is meaningful and effective for you. Close your eyes to activate your imagination. Visualize, in as detailed a way as possible, physical stress leaving your body. If you're not a visual person by nature, then feel the stress leaving your body.

Another gesture that connects you to people remarkably well to increase rapport and connection is to match the tilt of your patient's head. For example, if their head is tilted to their left, move yours in the same direction. Nonverbally this conveys more interest on your part, that you have noticed this slight detail, and you are attuned to them. With one head at a slight tilt and the other straight up and down there is a slight feeling of disconnect. Experimentally, try tilting your head in the opposite direction and notice how awkward that feels. If using body language to communicate does not come naturally to you, start by examining others first. Begin to notice how people stand in relation to each other in a variety of situations. Observe those postures you perceive as defensive or nonproductive and those that are appealing and favorable. My suggestion is to have fun experimenting in casual situations first, to discover what works best for you and what gets the best response from the children.

Have Fun with Facial Expressions

Okay, let's get ready to really have some fun. Kids absolutely love animated, over-exaggerated facial expressions. Cartoons are full of eyes popping out of their heads or rolling in circles, hair coming off their head about three feet, and mouths that are so shocked they open and fall all the way down to the floor — the more exaggerated the better. While we are not quite that capable, our faces hold a tremendous ability to communicate almost anything.

West Buncombe Elementary School in Asheville has a poster hanging in the hallway of a movie character named Ernest, who is popular with the kids. The poster shows Ernest demonstrating fifteen different facial expressions for captions such as surprised, scared, happy, etc. His expressions are delightfully comical. Likewise, Jim Carrey has made an entire career for himself based off that sole ability. I saw him being interviewed on television once and he told the host how he used to practice animated facial expressions in the mirror for hours.

Our faces hold so much energy, and, because it's the first thing we see when we meet someone, it almost exclusively makes our first impression. In pregnancy, women have often been described as "glowing," or a beautiful woman's face as "radiant." We give practical jokes away because we "couldn't keep a straight face," and our mom could always tell when we "looked guilty" of something. Maybe we looked like the "cat that swallowed the bird." How many times have we heard the saying, "I could tell by the look on your face"? Psychics "read the lines in our face," businessmen have "a look of confidence," gamblers have a "poker face," and you can look like "you've just seen a ghost." Our faces are very revealing, and this is especially true with young, intuitive children. It's hard to hide what you're thinking and feeling without your facial expressions giving it away.

On the other hand, we all know people who don't have energy at all moving through their face. Then we say they have a flat affect, a blank expression or a stone-cold face. Have you ever heard the expression, "They look like somebody sucked all the energy out of their face"? No energy is there and you can't tell what's going on inside that person at all. It's like they're hiding their emotions or perhaps unwilling or unable to show them.

Kids love expression and, if you are so inclined, a slightly exaggerated look can go a long way. We can tell the whole story of how we are thinking, perceiving and expecting by how we carry our expressions. Have fun with this. Use this as a way to lighten situations and make a connection with a child when appropriate. A meaningful radiant smile right from the start can go a long way.

It amuses me when the fear is so big, but the wound is so small. Typically, I start looking all over the place with an exaggerated look of being perplexed or confused while trying to find the wound. This was always a game with my daughter, Nicole, when she was young. She would fall down, hurt herself and start crying, making a big deal out of a little hurt. I would intentionally over-react with a look of exaggerated concern and then massage the wrong leg on purpose.

"Dad, it's over here," she would say pointing to a spot on her other leg. Then I would gently love and massage the correct leg but in the wrong place. I would look "oh so surprised" when she kept redirecting me. By the time she got through explaining it all, we were laughing so hard she wanted to, "do it again." Even though Nicole is nineteen now and all too familiar with the routine, we still get a kick out of it every now and then.

Your facial expressions will come forth quite naturally without having to be overly conscious about them when your intention is clear. In the example with my daughter, being silly and having fun took over the look on my face. In a medical setting, each interaction will call upon you to react and behave in a manner appropriate to the situation. Trust yourself. Remember, the energy and the message you carry in your expressions will be closely watched and will reflect the kind of situation *you* perceive the child to be in. We are giving them a chance to copy and adopt our perspective as their perspective, without saying a single word. Enough will be said through our facial expressions alone.

So be alert to what you are creating and be creative in what you choose to express. Relax, be yourself, and as always, have some fun.

Use Gentle Eye Contact

I have frequently found that making eye contact with the child when first entering the room helps to establish in the child that I'm there for them. Then, I make eye contact with the parents. A distinct message is emanated through your eyes from what is behind your eyes and is driven entirely by your...well, you know, intentions.

I was recently involved in a personal development group. We were exploring things in our past that still have an impact on our adult life. Part of one exercise was to sit in a circle and share with the group leader our presence, through just looking. John was our group leader, and he voluntarily drove five to six hours a day, every day for a week, just to be with us. He was not paid and I had a hard time understanding why he would do that. He had shared in our training and witnessed us working through our personal obstacles in an effort to be free of self-imposed limitations. It was an intense experience as each of us shared deeply personal events in our lives over a five-day period.

On the last day, the program director asked us to sit in a circle and face our group leader and silently, without words, thank him by looking into his eyes. There were about eight of us. We were all truly appreciative of his direction and his willingness to spend so much time with us despite working and having a family. He made time for us. Now in that circle was our chance to say through our eyes only, "Thank you." John could tangibly see in the eyes of everyone emotions like appreciation, love, gratitude and pride to the extent that he started sobbing from happiness. The love projected so powerfully through our gaze that he felt overwhelmed with tears of joy. It was easy for me to see, just then, exactly why he had volunteered in the first place. All this transpired in complete silence.

Eyes truly are windows to the soul and can be very revealing. When a healthcare worker loves his or her work, it shows. In fact it can't be helped. Love projected through the eyes from a sensitive heart sends a powerful message from the deepest core of our spirit. We have the ability to look into and right through each other to the nucleus of who and what we are in that moment. When we're in the right place within ourselves we don't want to conceal it (we don't have a choice, really); rather, we want to share all that we have and it overflows out of abundance on its own.

Withdrawing eye contact, however, can be considered an insult. "He won't even look at me," is a common expression, as if the person is not deserving of even being looked at. It can also appear to many people as if you're trying to hide something from them. You may appear insecure or unwilling to reveal yourself to them for some reason.

I saw a job interview take place with an emergency room physician who met with seven other physicians and showed up wearing dark sunglasses. The meeting went on for over one hour, and he never removed them! He was seeking employment while hiding from them at the same time. Naturally, after the interview the first question that arose for all the physicians was, "What did he have to hide?" Not looking directly into the eyes of those you care for sends a distinct nonverbal message as well.

I have witnessed nurses who were so disgusted with the poor care the parents gave their own child, that they expressed that disgust by completely withdrawing eye contact, like the parents weren't even there. It came across as a powerful passive-aggressive nonverbal statement, just watching it happen from across the room. I felt the uncomfortable energy it produced, and it wasn't even directed at me.

When Richard Nixon and John F. Kennedy had their televised presidential debate, newspaper commentaries described Richard Nixon as evasive. They weren't referring to how he answered questions, but in how his eye movements were perceived. It seems this created some degree of doubt in those covering the story. Further, if a person is perceived as shifty-eyed, that can easily create mistrust. When your eyes lack focus, it looks like all kinds of thoughts are running around in your head and the message you're sending becomes unclear. For most people, this kind of disjointed nonverbal message just feels uncomfortable.

The other extreme to watch for is over-empowerment. As if to say, "Look into my eyes, you're getting sleepy." No one wants to feel overpowered or overwhelmed by eye contact that's too aggressive. Just ask any woman what she finds displeasing or offensive when certain men look or stare at her with a penetrating glare.

With children, a strong look in your eyes about something on your mind that may not even be related to them can cause alarm. I have found that prolonged eye contact (even if it's gentle) while asking for cooperation, is often viewed as an aggressive command, a stare-down, or a challenge of wills. Rapport will be lost in those moments. You want a partnership, not a power trip. Avoid looking in such a way that may seem too insistent. I have found that removing eye contact at the point of asking for cooperation appears to decrease the intensity of the request. Asking for that cooperation without directly looking into another person's eyes, becomes more like an option rather than a command. You're giving them a chance to cooperate on their own using nonverbal persuasion. With an invitation, children feel they have a choice. The power to say yes or no remains in their hands because you're asking for their help. If the child gets to keep his or her power by making a choice whenever possible, you create a powerful ally, a welcoming friend.

Be sensitive to the fact that children are at a disadvantage. They are in your home court, the medical facility. You're bigger, smarter, and you're more powerful. So don't be surprised if they suddenly agree to follow your lead, or go the other way and initially reject your presence altogether. Be patient. You're viewed as the expert in these matters. Relax, and share with children, through your eyes, what brought you to your profession in the first place. Use your eyes as a way to make conversation that leads to a feeling of connection. Learn how to reach in and connect while you're looking, rather than just looking to see. The rest comes on its own.

Create Excitement with Your Physical Energy Level

Because children are so sensitive, even being tired or exhausted can be easily misunderstood as a general disinterest in working with them. It was not surprising to me to overhear a coworker describe how a young patient she was caring for misinterpreted her fatigue by believing she was responsible for causing it. Remember how easily children internalize circumstances. Your low physical energy can sometimes drain their physical energy, and feeling drained is not what we want them to copy. We don't want to appear to have little interest in them. Communicating to the young children you work with is something never to take for granted.

Years ago, I worked with a pediatric endocrinologist who would often make a direct association with your physical energy level and your level of interest in working with his children. I once heard him tell a very excellent nurse that she could use a little more enthusiasm in working with his children. He was referring to his perception of her physical energy level. I knew this nurse well and she had a lot of enthusiasm. The doctor found it hard to see because she wasn't as energetic about working with his young patients as some of the other nurses. Children can make the same mistake.

Enthusiasm and high energy are contagious and often fun to be around. They portray a level of excitement within you. This simple fact makes such a positive nonverbal statement all on its own. Often, children want to share in that excitement and be with you in a cooperative spirit because of it. It's as if they don't want to miss out on joining the fun, so they copy your physical energy level and get excited right along with you. Enthusiasm and high energy can easily show up as a willingness and a readiness to deal with anything, as if you're already prepared when you enter the room. As always, each situation needs your assessment as to how much physical energy and enthusiasm is appropriate to display. I have frequently gained immediate cooperation from sick or injured kids just by entering the room with an upbeat sense of energy and an enthusiastic smile. It can easily convey the simple message that you're glad to be there with them and willing to do all that you can to help.

When you love your work, it's funny how even challenges at the end of a long day won't leave you feeling tired. Consider this: feeling tired is a state of mind. Think about it. If your work is not fulfilling, it's the lack of fulfillment that tires you. It may actually be more mental fatigue than physical. Haven't you noticed that when you're involved in something you're passionate about you can go on forever? You're nourished by your work, not drained by it. Each encounter gives something back to you energetically, and often the interactions can be invigorating. I think kids have an uncanny ability to understand all this on some subtle level to the point that it affects how they choose to respond to you.

One day, I had a series of adult patients who complained bitterly, needed to cry and expressed an overabundance of negative emotions. When I got off of work and shared the day's experience with a friend, he asked me, "How can you listen to all that negativity all day long and not be affected by it?"

"I just know which energy is mine and which isn't," I replied.

The times I do feel drained are the times I have carelessly given permission to let that happen and have to take responsibility for that. I have found complaining or blaming to be two of the biggest energy drains. When you disempower yourself in this way, you feel helpless and at a loss, which just dissipates your physical energy. A few suggestions that have helped me when I feel this way are to ask for help from my coworkers when needed. I'll take a short break, make sure I've had something healthy to eat, and then consciously return to a state of mental appreciation or thankfulness.

We can't always expect to be at our best, so when your physical energy is truly low, share that with your patients so they understand and don't assume they have something to do with it. After all, if kids can make a game out of just about anything, why can't we? Consider telling them a story if appropriate. "There once was this tired nurse who had a very interesting day…"

Realize Your Mental State Is Transparent

We have all heard the expression "You are what you eat." I'd like to add, "You show what you think." It's not hard to read minds at all. Not always, of course, but how easy is it to tell what someone's thinking by the look on their face? The mind-body connection is especially apparent there. Your thinking shows up on your face through definite facial expressions. When someone is thinking in terms of doubt, is it not written all over their face and the drifting away of their eyes? We read into how they look and we think, "They're not buying it." Just thinking about pain, not even feeling it, causes a facial grimace to surface. Ask someone the food they hate the most, and when they conjure up that mental image watch what happens to how they express themselves.

Recently, Ryan, a seven-year-old in my neighborhood, fell off his bike and fractured his left shoulder. When his father, Chuck, drove him to the hospital, they immediately took x-rays. Several nurses and two doctors stood around the view screen as the x-ray film was put up for evaluation. What Chuck remembers most is the look on the faces of the medical staff.

"I got so scared when I saw the look on all their faces. I didn't think it was that bad up until then," he said. Apparently, the fracture was severe. The bone was splintered, and the nurses and the doctors must have been thinking something like, Wow, what a mess. How long is it going to take to fix that? Three and one-half hours of surgery, from midnight to 3:30 A.M., and two pins later is what that thought must have been. It was obviously reflected in their faces at the time. Over the next few days, as Chuck was processing the whole medical experience, he repeated that part of the story to me several times. For him with all that happened, the greatest fear he experienced came when seeing the look on the faces of the doctors and nurses when evaluating his son's injuries. That had the greatest impact and stayed in his memory the longest. Perhaps the urgency and severity, openly conveyed, aided in getting everyone rallied to respond to the need for on-call surgery in the middle of the night. But that's not how Chuck looked at it.

What I'm saying here is that there may be times when we, as healthcare practitioners, can be more sensitive and aware of the extent of our impact. Our patients are watching us very closely. Chuck copied the nurses' and doctors' concern. He held and carried their momentary expression of fear for days afterward.

Although we should never be expected to be perfect, we can learn from these situations. A poker face while thinking, wow, what a mess, is appreciated by our patients and their families much more than you may realize.

We must remember that our mental state is transparent and that the mind-body connection is oftentimes overtly obvious to those around us. In a state of fear our patients' senses are already heightened. Because of this, they have the tendency to read meaning in the minutest detail. In situations such as this, we can almost pretend our thoughts are literally handwritten across our forehead, completely exposed for all to see. We can actually use this knowledge to our advantage and be more aware of our expressions while our patients are observing us. In contrast, in situations that are not so severe, downplaying our concern can work just as powerfully.

Just thinking of my patients' well-being and the compassion I hold for them as I stand by their side sends a powerful message even in thought form. This kind of nonverbal message can have a reassuring impact on our patients even when situations take a turn for the worst. Perhaps, that's just when it's needed the most.

Use Touch to Speak Volumes

Touch transmits a distinct message. A reassuring hand on the shoulder, a pat on the back, a handshake or hug, can break the barriers of separation and help foster a sense of togetherness. It says, "I care about you, and I am comfortable being close to you." In essence, it speaks volumes. Because of that, touch hastens the rapport process in people we have never met before. Children welcome it and frequently associate it with affection. Families close to one another make frequent close physical contact, and your willingness to engage in a gentle touch associates you with that close inner circle. As a touch junkie myself, the need to express touch in order to waste no time in getting connected is immediate. An elaborate, silly handshake, slappin' 'em five, or a quick rub on the back on first introductions brings warmth, lightens the mood and shares a little of who you are. A gentle hand placed on the back of the shoulder of the child while talking to the parents can help to create a connection with the entire family as well.

As nurses and healthcare workers, our license authorizes us to touch professionally. Touching comes with the territory and carries different meanings in different situations. The quality of our touch and the message it conveys is again a direct reflection of our intentions. As nurses, we touch supportively, respectfully and diagnostically. Palpating and touching are a required part of our examination and physical assessment skills. We can also have that magic touch. Oftentimes, touching is expected of us from our patients, even more so than from the physician. In old-school nursing, we were trained to give back rubs to reduce stress, relieve tension and create professional rapport. Now we click the mouse with much more frequency! It's unfortunate we've been taken away from this type of contact by the demands of time, increased technical responsibilities and overwhelming nurse-to-patient ratios.

When it comes to physical contact, adults seem to have more personal space issues than children, but both have their individual comfort zones. If you sense this is present, honor that, so your touch is not perceived as an intrusion. Touch, to me, translates into trust. When a child is afraid, they often don't want anyone to come too close or even to look at an injury until they're perceived as

152

being trustworthy. A gentle touch elsewhere on the body can help create that feeling of safety. Should the art of touch be of particular interest to you, consider an in-depth look at other modalities. These include Therapeutic Touch, Healing Touch, Reiki, Huna and Qigong.

The modality of Healing Touch for example, embraces the element of healing but does not imply that the person doing the touching is responsible for it. Healing may simply happen in the combined presence of you and the person you're working with. You become an active observer, a witness to it.

My own experience came one day after teaching a class on the art of suggestion. I came home with a headache. One student in particular was having a bad day and was affecting my class adversely. I handled the situation well, but came home with this symptom. My wife, Lydia, who has been involved in Healing Touch for many years, held her hands on my head and then just a few inches above it. Immediately, my headache disappeared. I had never experienced pain leave so abruptly, so suddenly before. It was almost like it wasn't mine and didn't belong there in the first place!

Touch can be very powerful to those who are receptive to it. Don't under-estimate what it can accomplish for both you and your patients.

I'll share another example of how touch can be used. We live in the country and spend a lot of time landscaping in our flower gardens. Insect stings are a recreational hazard. Bee and wasp nests are built around us all the time, and I get stung almost once a year. I go inside, apply ice, pop a Benadryl and go back to work. The redness and swelling lasts a few days and then it itches before it goes away completely. I watched Lydia's treatment on herself one day after a wasp stung her on her leg. She held her hand a few inches over the sting and gently massaged back and forth over the area, never actually touching the skin. Her leg never got swollen and the redness was gone later that day! It worked far better than the drowse of pharmacology. It also helps us to draw upon our own innate abilities to heal ourselves.

Keeping this work alive by incorporating it into our own daily life makes it that much more powerful when we share our touch and ourselves with our patients. The work carries far more meaning when it's lived, rather than technically dispensed.

It seems I have had a lot to say about mannerisms that don't use words to communicate. I hope that by now you have come to realize that at times you can actually say so much more through nonverbal communication than with words alone. A gesture speaks paragraphs, your eyes communicate chapters and your touch can speak volumes. Use them all, but wield them with love.

SUMMARY

1) *Have a Clear Intention*

   All that you truly think, feel and believe becomes naturally apparent in how you express yourself. What you hold as your true intention will be the foundation for all the nonverbal messages you send.

2) *Create Calm with Body Posture/Gestures*

   Even your physical body can be used as a powerful vehicle to convey the compassion you feel in your heart for the kids you work with. If you're feeling any tension in your body, deliberately release it before sharing your presence with children in fear. Use soft hand gestures to direct the child where you want them to physically move in the room, to facilitate their procedure and to subtly gain their cooperation.

3) *Have Fun with Facial Expressions*

   Children absolutely love silly and exaggerated facial expressions, so use them to your advantage. More often than not, it makes them smile and can be an easy way to make an immediate and favorable connection with the kids.

4) *Use Gentle Eye Contact*

   Share the love you feel for the work you do through your eyes. When you walk into the room to meet a child and their family, make eye contact with the child first and then greet everyone else. Establish in the mind of the child that you're there for them first by giving them your immediate attention.

5) *Create Excitement with Your Physical Energy Level*

   Enthusiasm is highly contagious and enjoyable to be around. Children will often join you in a cooperative spirit so they too can be part of the fun and excitement enthusiasm creates.

6) *Realize Your Mental State Is Transparent*

   What we are thinking is communicated to the patient through our facial expressions. Be alert to this when patients are watching. Remember, the senses of a child or parent are hypervigilant in a state of fear. Even in thought form we can create a calming reassurance.

7) *Use Touch To Speak Volumes*
    Our touch can easily transmit layers and layers of meaningful information. Honor the personal space of those you work with. Many patients, especially children, expect some degree of personal contact in a medical setting. Touch with a loving intention.

*Nonverbal language speaks,
at times, even louder
than words themselves.*

— ⊠ ◊ ⊠ —

"The most beautiful thing we can
experience is the mysterious."
–Albert Einstein

— ⊠ ◊ ⊠ —

10: Use Your Intuition

*T*alk about a popular subject! The number of books, classes and courses on medical intuition have increased dramatically. What we have come to realize is that everybody has it, not everyone uses it, and anyone can learn to develop it — hence its current popularity. It's no longer reserved for the chosen few, even though rare individuals do exist who have a keener sense than average. We all have the ability to learn how to become sensitive enough to allow the intuitive aspect in our life to unfold. We don't have to be born with exceptional intuitive skill, we can be taught.

Experience in any profession naturally lends itself to the ability to anticipate responses and reactions in colleagues, customers and patients. That's why you chose the work you do to begin with. Something about the work resonates with you, you feel an affinity toward it and that "something" is based in your intuition. Most authors and trainers agree: you must learn to trust your instincts when you hear the voice of intuition. When intuition first begins to enter your life, a common tendency is to disregard or invalidate it. You may even consider yourself incapable of it, discounting the sense altogether and passing the feeling off as a mere coincidence.

Intuition Does Not Come from the Mind

Logically, rationally and analytically, intuition makes no sense so don't expect it to. The logical aspect of your mind will talk you out of the very possibility. To some extent, this doubt is only natural. Natural because our society has moved away from living close to nature, to Mother Earth, where intuition played a vital daily role in human survival. Now, we have moved, and very suddenly, into technological advancements, mechanization and computerization. Technology has become so integrated into our daily lives that we have come to rely on it more than on ourselves. Studies and hard technical data along the information superhighway have taken on much more meaning in our lives and have become the new standard approach. The explosive growth and the accelerated pace of technology and pharmacology lead us to look outside ourselves for answers. Living in that environment can diminish our ability to look within to tap into our natural, God-given talents and abilities.

Don't listen to the doubt. Learn to listen instead for the meaning of the intuitive message that comes to you. Then act from your heart. Also, pay close attention to the timing of your intuition with how important it is to act quickly. Experiment with listening to your intuition in minor situations with little consequences first.

As an example, I was in line at the hospital cafeteria. Next to me was a man who had a nervous energy about him. We both bought coffee, then moved over to an area to mix our cream and sugar. I just knew this man was going to spill his coffee. Without delay I listened to the impulse and took one step back. The timing was perfect, because in that exact moment he did indeed knock over his cup, and had I not acted on my insight, it would have spilled all over me. How many times have you heard yourself say, "I knew that was going to happen"? And how many times did you listen to and act on what you knew? The more we listen, the more we get in tune with the frequency of receiving it. The more we ignore and invalidate our own inner voice, the faster it recedes into dormancy as an unnecessary instinct. It becomes like a vestigial organ, an appendix, recognized by the body as no longer needed.

Learn to warm up to intuition in situations that can be experimentally fun. As you grow in familiarity, learn to slowly incorporate it into your work. Often times, our gut responses, if not surprisingly dead-on or accurate in detail, are usually in the ballpark.

Intuitively, you begin to know with children how to reach them, make a connection and feel rapport instantly. You begin to trust and allow the intuitive sense to guide your actions and approach into creating a cooperative partnership with children. In working with Tom, the seven-year-old I described earlier in the section on body posture, it was intuition that led me to so quickly enter his close personal space and sit right next to him as my initial approach. It was my intuitive belief we didn't need the buffer of a warm-up conversation, and that we had the ability to connect instantaneously. It paid off. He followed my instructions to the letter and jumped on the fast track to a positive hospital experience. Kids respond intuitively without even knowing what it's called. It's so natural for them. I have observed many children completely unwilling to let a whole medical team help them, and then suddenly they single out one person in the room and say, "Only if it's you!"

Trust Your Instincts

I was making rounds one night as a supervisor at Larkin General Hospital in Miami, Florida. It was around 1 A.M. when I entered the Intensive Care Unit to get a brief report on the night's activities. Tim, a staff RN, shared his concern with me about a surgical patient he was caring for who was experiencing post-operative bleeding. The surgery had been completed about six hours prior.

Tim had already notified the surgeon, who had told him, "We expect some bleeding." This particular surgery was known for that, according to the doctor, so the concern was noted and deemed unnecessary to act upon. Tim felt he had fulfilled his responsibility by notifying the surgeon, and they mutually agreed the patient was not in any danger. I did not have the opportunity to see the bleeding for myself, but we weighed pads to assess how much bleeding was actually taking place. Patients experiencing blood loss in an ICU setting is not uncommon. At this point I hadn't examined the patient. Something about Tim's tone of voice, how he relayed the story and described the bleeding, caused an immediate sense of alarm within me.

"Get the doctor back on the phone," I said, "and tell him again what you saw and describe it in the same way you just did with me."

"I already did that," Tim said.

I paused a moment, then said, "Please do it again."

The patient's vital signs gave no indication of any trouble. The heart monitor showed normal sinus rhythm and the patient himself had no symptoms to report. That should have been enough to relieve my concern. It wasn't.

Thirty minutes later, Tim said the physician called back, noted Tim's repeated concern restating, "We expect this type of bleeding."

"He was really annoyed at being awakened again with the same information," Tim said.

By this time, my concern had made an impression on another nurse who started to sense something too. For the third time in an hour, we contacted the doctor, only this time I called. He was angry, and proceeded to tell me the exact same thing, word for word, that he had already told Tim, twice. I insisted he come in and see the patient for himself. By now, he was furious and started yelling about his early morning operating room schedule. Somehow, against the odds, I managed to get him to agree to come in even though he knew little about my professional judgment.

After assessing the situation for himself the surgeon said, "Call in the OR team, I need to go back in now." It was 3 A.M.

What we eventually found out was that the patient's life would not have been saved if we had waited until morning. He was not only bleeding externally but internally as well. By the time his symptoms were overt, it would have been too late.

Believe me, I took a lot of heat initially for following up on that intuitiveness. If I had been wrong, my reputation would have suffered badly, especially in a small hospital where everybody knows and talks about each other. My credibility with that physician as a responsible supervisor with critical assessment skills would have been shot. I went out on a limb, not only by standing behind my belief but by not backing down from it. I trusted my instincts even when confronted by an angry, well-known, cross-examining surgeon at two in the morning. Had I not stayed firm and determined in knowing what I believed to be true, I may not have conveyed my concerns in a way that convinced the surgeon to respond as he did. The combination of the certainty in the tone of my voice and my persistence is what he responded to, more than the statistical data we provided him concerning the patient's status. I know what I responded to. I would have felt completely responsible for the loss of that life if I had ignored my gut, taken only the required action, and accepted the combined assessment of the patient's assigned nurse and surgeon. I could have waited three more hours for an operating team that was going to come in anyway. I didn't. I wasn't going to live with what I knew would have been a bad judgment call on my part. No one would have blamed me either, but I would have blamed myself. Getting a bad reputation, losing credibility and suffering embarrassment would have been a lot easier to live with compared to what I sensed was going to happen to this patient had I not intervened. That was just plain common sense to me at the time.

Intuition speaks to us with varying degrees of intensity. To me, listening to that one was obvious. It was a shout inside. The challenge lies in listening to the little whispers we ignore that only later we recognize as a beneficial message.

On a lighter side, my mother-in-law often told me her secret to winning with frequency at the Greyhound Racetrack in Miami. When you're in line to buy tickets and you get a hunch on a number, always buy two tickets, the one you were going to buy and one on the hunch!

Learn to go with your intuitive feeling on how to approach, what to say and the easiest way to connect with each child. Trust yourself and trust the process.

Embrace the Mystery

Bud was a man I worked with at the South Florida Artificial Kidney Center in 1978. This outpatient renal dialysis center served about thirteen patients at a time. I was employed as a registered nurse and had to learn about the technology, the equipment and patient symptomatology. Two needles were placed in the patient's access site in their arm. One, to withdraw large volumes of blood where it was pumped through a hollow fiber artificial kidney to remove waste products, and then returned to the patient's blood stream through the second needle. The average dialysis time was four to six hours.

Every fifteen minutes we made scheduled rounds, checked pressure readings and took vital signs. Bud had just completed his rounds as he walked along the row of patients, which spanned about fifty feet. He shared the following story with me:

163

Something made me go all the way back to the very first patient I already checked, he said. I had no reason to, but I followed the feeling anyway. When I got there, I saw that one of the access needles had fallen out of the patient's arm and was lying on the floor in-between two chairs. The pump was sucking massive amounts of air into the system and by the time I got there, there were only about eighteen inches of blood left in the return line going into the patient's blood stream with air right behind it! I grabbed a clamp and shut the system down. I looked over at the patient and he was sound asleep.

The patient would have suffered a massive air embolism and died within seconds had Bud not been there with his uncanny timing.

Bud repeated over and over, "I don't know what made me go back there... I don't know what made me go back there."

The logical, rational, analytical aspect of Bud's mind continued to question him even in the face of saving someone's life! If any of these things made sense to us, as to how we know these things, it wouldn't be called intuition. It's all a matter of how much you want to open yourself up to this aspect of patient care and be available to it. Some of us are naturally more receptive than others. Part of its development within you depends upon experience in your profession and trusting the judgment calls that come to you.

My wife is a nursing instructor for Western Carolina University and works with nursing students during their clinical rotation in the hospital. One of her students went into the room of a patient who had requested pain medication. This patient was officially assigned to the hospital's regular nursing staff, and the nursing student was there secondarily to participate in patient care, help out and learn nursing skills. In collaboration with the patient's assigned and experienced nurse, the student was allowed to administer a dose of intravenous morphine. The patient's vital signs had been stable. Lydia instructed her student in how to obtain and document the withdrawal of the controlled substance from the locked narcotic cart. Then the student nurse went with the patient's assigned nurse to administer the medication.

"I don't know what made me follow them to the patient's room," she said. "I had plenty of work to do with my other students, and the patient didn't need three nurses to give a routine pain medication." When she got there, the student nurse was just about to administer the dose.

"Before giving that medicine, check the blood pressure again," Lydia requested. The patient's blood pressure had suddenly dropped. The reading? 80/40! With the administration of a high dose opioid, the patient would have very likely experienced a cardiopulmonary arrest.

Afterward, I heard the words, "I don't know what made me follow them to the patient's room," for the next few days.

Whenever I hear someone say those words, it helps me to remember that intuition comes from our gut and not from our head. Get comfortable not knowing the how or why and just accept it.

Personally, I don't claim to know very much about intuition, how it works, or what makes it come to us when it does, but I *know* that it does. Somehow it's part of the work we do. I know we can't explain it very well, and that it comes from faculties other than rational logic. Analytically, we will question it, even in the face of it saving someone's life right before our eyes. When it descends upon you, don't ignore or invalidate it. Embrace the mystery. Use the best judgment you have keeping your patient's best interest in mind. As long as you do that, you can never go wrong.

Experience is a valuable teacher and will undoubtedly intensify your ability to tap into your source of intuition. You have to learn how to respond to it in the moments it responds to you. You have to find your own way. There is no other way. Be patient and let it come naturally. When you learn to recognize its distinct inner voice, listen to it carefully, and trust the response you are guided to take.

SUMMARY

1) Intuition can be naturally present within you or develop through experience in your profession. Listen to the message it brings rather than the natural tendency to ignore or invalidate its presence.

2) Learn to respond to intuition in the moments it responds to you. Trust the action you're guided to take.

3) Begin to act on small insights that are of minor consequence to help develop your confidence. This will help you to be open and receptive to even greater challenges.

4) Don't even try to explain it when it comes to you. Just accept the mystery. (Somehow...I know you will!)

Intuitively, you begin to know with children how to reach them and make a connection. Trust and allow your intuitive sense to guide your actions and approach into creating a cooperative partnership.

"Let the air breathe for you."
–Emmett Miller, M.D.

11: Breathe in Tranquility

*I*n 1981 I traveled to India. I fell in love with the culture and lived there for three months. It was a spiritual journey, deeply embracing the magnificent religious history of the country and the living spiritual force it's known for. In Poona, about four hours by car from Bombay (honking the horn all the way), I met an eastern Indian mystic named Bhagwan Shree Rajneesh in his ashram. At first, seeing him from the outdoor audience in Buddha Hall, he looked too ordinary to me. After having traveled halfway around the world to get there, the American in me needed more of a sensation.

As I began the enculturation process, I slowly opened myself to new ways of being, and I left the rushing, fast-paced, right-now American mind behind and gradually settled in. As things slowed down, so did my breathing and so did my thinking. Suddenly, I became more receptive to subtleties. Things that were previously overlooked took on a whole new perspective.

When the day came to sit before Bhagwan face to face in personal dialogue, I was filled with anticipation and excitement. I watched as friends before me, one by one, were struck by the awe of their experience as they stumbled to their feet as if divinely drunk. Then it was my turn. "Awe" is a poorly defined word from this perspective. No word or words could be used, no matter how much I would like to accurately describe or share with you that experience. What I can say is that sitting in the presence of this man, looking into his eyes and experiencing his breathing was an entrancement. It was other-worldly. I have never before felt such a profound sense of peace and tranquility in my entire life. His breathing was slow, rhythmic, musical and almost imperceptible. It danced with a calmness and inner peace I have never witnessed or

169

participated in before. It was pure and magical. I was helped to my feet by two people and then gently moved over to the side. I still sat very close as I continued to watch him. No wonder so much emphasis is placed on breath in the Eastern World. Only later did I realize I was privileged in experiencing it from the source. Needless to say, the experience was very profound.

I often joke with friends I have shared this story with by saying, "I know I don't look like someone capable of having a profound experience, but nevertheless I did."

Since then, using breath with my patients and myself has carried exceptional meaning. I learned through that personal experience the tremendous impact and calming effect deep breathing can carry, by relaxing into it and being in its presence. Although my breathing is not as evolved, I can make attempts to impart the knowledge and benefits of that experience. If nothing else, I have often stood at many a patient's bedside and intentionally and audibly exercised slow, deep abdominal breathing without saying a word. Neurolinguistic programming calls this "pacing." It gives patients something tangible and powerful to copy, yet at the same time it's subtle. The effect always seems to be a reduced level of fear or tension. The breath goes all the way down two inches below the belly button. The Japanese have named this point the "Hara" — our center. The chest rises very little, as the abdomen visibly moves up and down. If you want to see very natural deep belly breathing, watch an infant breathe. There's practically no chest movement.

I have demonstrated this way of breathing to middle school children by lying flat on the floor and placing a book on my abdomen. The book moves up and down with the abdomen to make more obvious how far down the breath goes while pointing out minimal chest expansion.

Fear, however, has no choice. It's obligated by our very physiology to show up as rapid and shallow in the chest. It's not possible any other way. The next time you're angry or afraid, become aware of the source of your breathing. You'll notice it's in the chest, rapid and shallow. Intentionally move your breath to your abdomen, slow and deep, and remain focused there. If you do, you cannot stay angry or afraid for very long. It will shift. It will change on its own, as a natural consequence, because fear and anger require a chaotic breathing pattern.

When we present ourselves to our patients, our breathing is subconsciously noticed. Being aware of this helps us to feel more centered and grounded by seeing to it that our own breath is in the right place when we are in the presence of our patients. Several slow, deep breaths or a pronounced sigh have always been used as preparation for many an important event. Yoga, rebirthing, Sufi and Tantric practices share profound stories of the power and depth of breath work.

Intentionally sharing your breathing is powerful and worth experimenting with. We can breathe with the intention to have a calming effect, first on ourselves and then with our patients.

For many years, actors have played with breathing style to augment the roles they portray. They know all the tricks. To jump into an angry, aggressive part, they intentionally breathe repeatedly, rapid and shallow within the chest. Immediately it becomes very easy to snap into an angry, aggressive role. Conversely, they know how to take on the "James Bond" persona to remain cool, calm and collected when completely surrounded by death and danger. They take the breath to the very bottom of the belly, as deeply as possible. Hold it a moment, then take a slow, prolonged exhale before playing the part.

For our patients whose breathing is out of control with pain or fear, methods can be used to help redirect it. Often our patients, overwhelmed with fear, are not even aware of the extent to which their breathing can be working against them. The approach I have used most successfully is to give the command "breathe here" while placing my hand on the patient's lower abdomen. Then I take slow deep breaths myself so that they can hear them. A very slow, very prolonged exhale, guarantees your next breath will be slow and deep. Other times, I have matched the speed of their breathing as a rapport method, loud enough for them to hear, and then gradually slowed it down to get them to do the same.

Hyperventilating has deleterious effects on the body's physiology. Breathing too fast blows off excessive carbon dioxide, leading to a respiratory alkalosis. Our PH rises in our arterial blood, as the bicarbonate, partial pressure of our arterial carbon dioxide, calcium and potassium levels all drop. Apprehension, a feeling of smothering, faintness and impaired consciousness are associated symptoms. One patient I cared for hyperventilated in the ER waiting room to the extent that she couldn't physically walk without my help.

On the other hand, deep abdominal breathing has its own physiology. It is theorized that the limbic system and areas in our cerebral cortex which affect emotion, are involved to produce the calming effect. Involuntary activities are stimulated, and brain wave patterns shift. Pulse, breathing and blood pressure drop.

It seems Western science agrees with Eastern experience. Breath powerfully exerts its effect on our body. For us, we combine both science and living experience as yet another tool to be used within ourselves and with those we serve. <Sigh>

SUMMARY

1) Don't underestimate how something as subtle as breath awareness can impact the well-being of your patients.

2) Deliberate, slow, deep abdominal breathing two inches below the belly button has a relaxing, peaceful effect within yourself and on those around you. Intentionally guide your patients to do the same when in a state of fear.

3) Physically touch your patients on the abdomen while instructing their breathing so they can feel the exact area you want them to focus on. This also aids in your rapport.

4) Fear cannot physiologically persist in the presence of slow, deep abdominal breathing.

> *If nothing else, while standing at the patient's bedside, audibly exercise slow, deep abdominal breathing.*

―•―◄•►―•―

"Let yourself be silently drawn by the
strange pull of what you really love.
It will not lead you astray."
–Rumi

―•―◄•►―•―

12: Enter the Innocence of Love and Spirit

*R*eturn with me now to the basics of innocence. Can you remember when you looked at things as a child and the spirit of wonderment reflected in your eyes? You were never in a hurry to know. Investigating was simply enough. Receptivity was a dominant force in your life that you never questioned. You were open and available from all sides of your being. Little energy was expended in doubt, and the possibilities, the willingness to believe, had no boundaries. Living in a little bit of everyday magic was routine, a normal part of your daily experience.

Standing next to that innocence as an adult enriches you, reminds you that our world, no matter how trepidatious, would be lost forever without it. Thank God innocence is alive in our children at least. It must be the polar opposite, the mandatory universal balance, to a world at war. Adults have so much to learn from every child they encounter. Perhaps success with frightened children comes most often to those who perceive themselves to be on equal ground in their presence. No one is superior and no one is inferior, no one the wiser and no one the more immature. The hierarchy dissolves when innocent souls stand together. Only a neutral territory and a passive receptive energy remain as the playground for the intervention of the divine expressed as love.

Enter the Spirit

There comes a point when you become the work and the work becomes you. The lines between what you do and who you are lose separation and melt together as one complete whole. Children start to naturally gravitate to you because of who you are and how you express yourself. To me, it feels as if you magically enter into a spiritual dimension where the normal laws of reason and probability don't always apply as one might expect. Somehow children manage to find you in and out of a medical setting.

One day, I was at the beach and caught up in the beauty of my surroundings. It was a magnificent bright, sunny day, there was a gentle breeze in the air, and the sky was amazingly blue. As I walked along and through the people on the beach, a woman crossed my path. She was obviously angry with her son, and she was verbally letting him have it, as he lagged behind her. He wanted something and mom, apparently, wasn't having it. As the boy walked past and then ahead of me, I playfully entered into the spirit of a child and in defense of the boy I thought to myself, Aww, come on, Mom. We're at the beach and having fun.... In that exact moment, he suddenly turned completely around to look at me. It was as if I had said it out loud and he heard me — the timing was so perfect! He slowed down and almost came to a standstill as he continued staring at me.

"Hurry up," his mother insisted.

It has been my experience countless times that the innocence of an open, receptive heart has spiritual roots. Your soul itself vibrates, and you feel so alive if even for brief instants. You become a magnet to the energy of children and they to you where like energies find themselves and draw near to one another.

As I continued to walk through the crowd and up to the open beach waters, I walked in knee-high and stood there taking in the breathtaking day. As I did, three children with broken English and obviously from a different country ran right up to me. The oldest boy, who was about ten years old, was so jubilant in his flailing expression of himself he almost ran right into me while looking into my eyes as if he was about to tackle a friend. Actually, I would have enjoyed that and wished he had, but he managed to restrain himself at the last moment and just ran into my left arm. Beaming with an exuberant smile, he stared into the horizon as he stood next to me. His younger brother splashed right behind us, but his little sister ran straight at me as fast as she could until she was forced to slow down when the water reached her chest. Our eyes met briefly. Her face was filled with the radiance of an angel and her smile was over-joyed. Her eyes were so brilliant, so alive, so profoundly dazzling, she looked as if she was looking at God himself in the form of an ocean. In that one concise moment, she shared the full contents of her very soul. God did come to visit us momentarily through the smiles and in the eyes of those children. I felt as if I had been given a blessing, a holy anointing at the altar as it came showering upon me completely uninvited and all on its own. I never stood at the altar with swimming trunks on before. It's my belief the children we meet who briefly enter our life are blessings in disguise no matter how they come to us.

As healthcare professionals dealing with people in pain and fear, nothing reaches us as deeply as the innocence of the human spirit.

Enter the Spirit through Love

I once worked with an eight-year-old boy who refused to take insulin shots. He came from a challenging social environment. His father was absent in his life and his mother was doing the best she could with two other children, and now her son was diagnosed with a chronic disease. On top of that he was phobic and had a morbid fear of needles. Over the days I spent educating this boy and his mother, our rapport seemed difficult to develop. Perhaps as a man my presence was an unpleasant reminder of what was missing in their lives. The day before he was to be discharged from the hospital I continued to try and break through his phobia about receiving injections, but he continued fighting me and resisted all my efforts. The only remaining tool, it seemed, was to just love this family in spite of all the physical, social and emotional obstacles they presented me with daily. I told the boy that not only did he need to take the shots, but that I wanted him to learn to give a shot to himself. I informed them both that the doctor relied on me to decide when they were educationally ready to safely care for his diabetes at home. At this point all I had left for them was my heart and the words that came through it. Then something unusual happened. He took the syringe I had prepared for him (as I had every day) right out of my hands, and he self-injected himself just as I had been teaching him but couldn't get him to do. He suddenly started dancing, singing and hopping all at once around his hospital bed. His mother and I looked at each other astonished by his newfound eagerness as he continued in his victory dance. His fear was finally broken. Days of interaction culminated into one atomic moment. Love broke through what nothing else could.

Children have an innate intuitiveness about them and are particularly sensitive to the sincere expression of love and a heart-first approach. I believe love opens the door to the dimension of spirit, and the dimension of spirit moves things within both the child and those who work with them. You become joined in a sacred bond where trust and fear cannot exist at the same time, just as you cannot inhale and exhale at the same time. Blessings a thousandfold enter and fill the entire room and all its occupants when a child's anxiety and fear are released. Sharing in the light of its presence becomes an honor. When it happens to you even once, it's never forgotten and becomes the standard by which all your interactions with frightened children are compared. With this as the foundation, you seek no other framework and ask for no further guidance. It becomes the basis from which all your intention originates. Your target, what you're aiming for, becomes crystal clear.

In the dimension of love, trust and security, redirecting a fear is made easier. Releasing the fear by simply becoming less willing to cling to it becomes more appealing to the child.

In the presence of someone who genuinely cares about what happens to me, it becomes more difficult to view the fear as beneficial. I can see the extent by which you stand by me and I can trust you, and then I *do* trust you.

Children can see through your hidden agendas and recognize if you're there for them or for your own reasons. They haven't had enough exposure over time to adults talking them out of that nature to pursue logic, intellect, competition and the importance of getting ahead in an adult world. That's why logical reasoning with children rarely works. Their primary experience of life is not through their head, it's through their heart.

So if a child is afraid of a monster hiding under the bed, even if you look together and logically see that no monster is there, the fear often continues imaginatively and emotionally. Love is the key to reaching that imagination and emotion. Share your sincerity and your heart-felt concern, and you start

178

reaching children in places that previously seemed impervious to rational thought.

One summer evening during a violent thunderstorm a mother was tucking her son into bed. She was about to turn off the light when he asked with a tremor in his voice,

"Mommy, will you sleep with me tonight?"

The mother smiled, gave him a reassuring hug and said, "I can't dear, I have to sleep in Daddy's room."

A long silence was broken at last by his shaky little voice, "The big sissy!"

Heart Medicine

All cultures have understood that an active, vibrating heart does things that don't look logical to the mind. St. Francis of Assisi would attract animals around him when he meditated by feeling the vibration of his own heart. Heart medicine is what it is called by Native American Indians. That is the meaning of the Sanskrit word "*Satsang*" — a wordless state of heart-to-heart communication, a communion. Heart has its own language and exists so naturally. Have you not looked into the eyes of your dog or cat and understood their exact need without a verbal dialogue? You know. The communication has already happened because heart has its own vibration that lends itself to being universally understood. Heart says, "I see what's happening to you and I want to help. I will do whatever it takes to be a part of the process of your well-being." A heart that is sensitive, aware and open to the state of another, vibrates much differently than if I approach you from the head with my intelligence, my thinking, my ego. In keeping with ego, no matter how good you are your work remains self-limited because you remain self-contained. As good as you are coming from there, you will never be as good as you can be. You close yourself off to the possibilities that go beyond you and you alone.

One of the more powerful experiences I have had over the years in relation to how deeply the energy of heart can penetrate our patients was with a man I cared for in the Intensive Care Unit. I was working the three-to-eleven shift and he had just returned from having extensive genitourinary surgery. I

179

recognized the man as someone I had taken care of in the past. He was a tall, very large man, gruff and unrefined in his mannerisms and in how he related to people.

I was in the "zone" that day as far as staying in the present moment and really enjoying my work. I wasn't thinking about being somewhere else; I was totally focused on my patient's needs and shared my compassion for this man in his present condition. He arrived from the operating room in four-point leather restraints (applied at the nurses' discretion), and was recovering from anesthesia and pain medicine. He had a Foley catheter inserted. It seemed that in a very short time we were able to establish a meaningful, personal connection based on trust. My intention and compassion found a unique combination to express itself in creating remarkable rapport. He knew I cared about his condition. His recovery progressed in stable fashion, and he no longer needed restraints, so I removed them. The remainder of my eight-hour shift with him went remarkably well. I gave report and left the unit but stayed to work the night shift as house supervisor.

At 3 A.M. my pager went off as I heard the overhead paging system call for security to report to the ICU, "stat." When I arrived, I saw this man standing out of bed swinging his arms at his nurse, who was backing up to protect himself while yelling at him to stop. He had pulled out his Foley catheter, and it was lying on the floor next to him.

Now if you are an experienced nurse you may say that at this point he had "sundowners," a term coined for otherwise cooperative patients who get confused and disoriented at night. They can become agitated and physically combative with you. Indeed he had, but I also came to find out he was having a reaction to the pain medicine Demerol, which he had just been given. Through all this, what happened next surprised even me. As I stood in the doorway to his room surrounded by several people and now a security guard, I called out his name. As he turned around, we made eye contact.

I wrinkled my face at him, put my hands on my hips and assertively asked, "What are you doing?" As soon as he saw me, he immediately came to his senses. He stopped fighting, turned around and sat down on his bed. Quietly, he allowed his restraints to be reapplied as the crowd dispersed. As unbelievable as it sounds, even through the side effects of his medicine, his confusion, agitation, and disorientation, something in our relationship broke through it all. Perhaps my earlier compassion for him had a lasting impact that he didn't forget even under all these adverse conditions. Fortunately, the patient managed not to injure himself or anyone else either.

When I was asked, "*How* did you do that?" I had no answer to give other than the intangible, yet amazingly powerful effect of heart medicine. The physical, emotional and mental environment a compassionate heart creates can accelerate the bonding process, foster trust and move mountains right before your eyes.

A similar instance happened to me early in my career as an orderly at Mercy Hospital in Buffalo. Security was called to a teenager's room; he was afraid and acting out belligerently. It just so happened that earlier that day we had met and made a brief, friendly connection. I was near his room when I heard the page, so I went to see what was happening. Several men who were giving him an ultimatum of some sort surrounded him and he was not giving in. He looked ready and willing to physically fight.

Through the crowd and from across the room I called out his name and said, "Look at me." As soon as our eyes met and he recognized me, he immediately stopped resisting and the situation was defused. His nurse followed me down the hall and wanted to know how I managed to reach him when no one else in the room could. At the time, I'm not sure even my own head knew what my heart was doing because my explanation was completely inadequate. Heart medicine, it seems is so simple to understand but yet so very difficult to explain. Perhaps in the presence of love and compassion the energy that was going into defenses, self-protection and fear are freed to go into a more creative direction. The lower vibrational energy pattern of fear gets an invitation from the higher vibrational energy pattern of love. When that love and compassion are genuinely expressed it's amazing how often people will take you up on your offer.

When two or more individuals are connected in this way, barriers drop and we are no longer individuals. We have become something far greater and are connected to a higher, more universal source. We meet on a higher plane of consciousness abundant in trust and simplicity.

These are the blessings I have felt and invite you to join. Thankfulness and honor is all that's left to be felt in its magical presence.

A four-year-old child lived next door to an elderly man who had just lost his wife. When the child saw the man crying, the little boy went over into the man's yard and climbed on top of the man's lap and sat there.

When the boy's mother asked him what he had said to the neighbor, the little boy said, "Nothing, I just helped him cry."

SUMMARY

1) A powerful binding force is created through the simplicity of a genuinely expressive heart.

2) Children recognize and respond to the sincere expression of love and are particularly sensitive to being approached heart-first.

3) Relate to the child on the simple plane of innocence and watch the grip of fear soften.

4) When you come from your own heart space naturally, you are connected to the higher universal source of spirit. More energy becomes available to you than just the child's and your own to transform the fear into trust.

Perhaps success with frightened children comes most often to those who perceive themselves to be on equal ground in their presence.

"We cannot do everything at once,
but we can do something at once."
–Calvin Coolidge

13: Additional Suggestions

Combine the Skills

*W*hen you start combining several of the skills we have discussed, you accelerate your effectiveness. Just being comfortable with yourself in the presence of frightened children, and determined in your intentions, will provide you with a powerful foundation to build even higher levels of satisfaction and success. From there, all your nonverbal expressions will comfortably emerge. Creating instant rapport and reshaping expectations through proper semantics, while intuitively approaching your patients, will start to happen quite naturally. It sounds like a lot to accomplish simultaneously but by practicing them individually, you'll find these skills start falling together on their own through your unique style of self-expression. With a little patience, combining the skills discussed in this book will be more spontaneous and you won't have to consciously think about each detail. To me, it's like entering into a playground full of opportunities to enjoy your work, and this work should be approached playfully. That, too, becomes yet another avenue with which to relate to the children.

In addition to combining what we have discussed thus far, try the following suggestions.

Use the Art of Distraction

Assisting children in the art of transforming their fear requires more than just distraction. But let's not forget just how powerful simple distractions can be. Giving the child a single moment of distraction is similar to using the mental shock technique I described earlier. It's just another way of interrupting the thought process long enough to give the mind a chance to consider a new direction. Whether or not the child acts on that consideration is directly proportional to the quality of your supportive relationship and your ability to develop immediate rapport. I have seen nurses successfully use everything from crayons to ambu-bags, books to stuffed animals, and medical equipment to just plain old conversation to shift a child's attention off one thing and onto another while performing their tasks.

For example, seven-year-old Jennifer was with her mother, and was so upset about getting her blood drawn that she was red in the face from crying, screaming and even kicking at the lab staff. Her overreaction created such a scene that her room was crowded with disbelieving coworkers by the time I arrived. I suggested the team stop any further interaction with her in an attempt to defuse the aggravated situation and give her a moment to calm down. I was in the middle of suggesting we change rooms to reset the environment, when the technician working with her gave her a cell phone to call her dad, whom she was crying out for. Talking to her father over the phone consumed all her extraneous energy and distracted her enough to allow the phlebotomist to draw her blood while she continued crying and talking to him. The only person she would let near her was the lab technician. This child had an involved social and medical history, and fortunately the lab staff was sensitive enough to consider her needs above and beyond the norm. Because this department also serves many special-needs children, the department director for the lab actually started the process of developing a written policy to protect his lab staff from "kids that kick." Through the use of a rather creative distraction, the phlebotomist skillfully handled a difficult situation.

Let the Parent Hold the Child

"We're going to need some help with this one," the anesthesiologist said about Brad, a four-year-old. He was all worked up and in a panic over having pre-op testing and being told about his upcoming surgery as he sat in the waiting room. His mother had to hold his hand and pull him along to see me so I could draw his blood. At least he's walking and not being carried, I thought to myself.

I took this as at least one positive sign, however small, in our relationship thus far. Walking toward me, Brad showed a faint glimmer of trust. I asked the mother to sit her son in her lap, and then I greeted the boy like he was my long-lost friend and immediately handed him a small package. He stopped crying and struggling in his mother's lap and took the tiny package from my hand.

"Will you open that for me?" I asked. Inquisitively he started to peel back the paper lid. "It's called a butterfly," I said, as I watched him reach in with his little fingers and hold the tubing and the tiny-capped needle in his hand. Our emphasis, however, was on the little blue wings that look like a butterfly. While sitting in the safety of his mother's lap, all his fear was momentarily diverted into curiosity. I immediately took it from his hand. After all, he was four years old and holding a needle in his hands given to him by a nurse in front of his mother. That has to be worse than running around the house with scissors!

"It works like this," I said, as I quickly swiped his arm with alcohol, applied a tourniquet and inserted the needle in his vein. He started to struggle but stopped when I said, "That's it, we're all done." He looked at me with disbelief that we were done so quickly and started to get up and leave (remember how literal kids are) with the needle still in his vein.

"Hold still just one more minute," I said, as I finished collecting his blood and removed the needle. He watched me intently the entire time. Judging by the look on his face, he was probably trying to figure out what a butterfly and a needle had to do with each other during the venipuncture.

"I don't believe it," his mother said, as he waited until I was done, and then together we picked out a colorful Band-Aid. The security of sitting in his mother's lap combined with a simple distraction was all he needed to hold still long enough to cooperate.

If You Have Time, Use It

Doctor Hendrix at Larkin General Hospital in Miami, Florida, once worked with a frightened seven-year-old boy named Kevin for over an hour in trying to convince him he wouldn't hurt him in order to suture closed his leg wound. The boy was alone and kept getting on and off the stretcher as the doctor refused to accept his fear and stood in front of him while persistently talking him down. Fortunately, he was the only patient in the ER and he could afford to spend the time.

He kept telling the child he wouldn't feel anything, because his leg would be made numb. He repeated himself so many times, and with such persistence that gradually the boy softened over time. I don't think he ever expected that kind of consideration. As far as time goes in emergency rooms, he was getting the royal treatment. I remained an observer and didn't interfere with the doctor who patiently developed his rapport. His intention was powerfully conveyed in his vocal tone and word choice but especially in his determined belief that this boy was going to have a good experience. Kevin eventually came to realize that the doctor was not going to accept it any other way. I believe the determination that I saw in Doctor Hendrix came from the father in him, as he had a son the same age as this boy.

Finally, the doctor's intention broke through and Kevin decided to cooperate, but as soon as he saw me open the suture kit and prepare the instrumentation, he started objecting all over again.

"Put that away," Dr. Hendrix said, as I had to hide the instrumentation around a curtain. Dr. Hendrix continually kept him engaged in conversation until it paid off. He had a syringe of lidocaine in his shirt pocket as he continued talking to him and the boy eventually held still and allowed the injection. He then took the needle and poked the edges of his wound he just made numb and asked the boy if he felt anything.

"No," he said. Doctor Hendrix then handed Kevin the syringe and asked him to touch his wound for himself. Kevin actually found the courage to poke the edges of his own wound with the needle. Finally, he allowed Dr. Hendrix to proceed with the closure. Total time elapsed: one hour and fifteen minutes. I know busy ERs can't always afford this approach, but if you have the time, use it.

Designate One Person to Stay at the Head of the Bed to Talk the Child Through

One of the more difficult experiences I had involved a five-year-old boy who came into the ER immobilized on a backboard in intense pain. He had fallen off his bike and fractured his femur and was delirious from the pain when EMS brought him in. He was alone, as attempts were being made to contact his parents. I was shocked, both to hear this child threaten us with varied forms of physical harm and by the language he was using if we touched him. He was operating out of pain, fear and survival instincts. In extreme emergencies or trauma situations, it helps to assign one primary person to communicate with the child. As the trauma team assembled around him, one nurse was designated to serve no other function other than to stay at the head of the bed and softly talk to him and to be exclusively available to care for his emotional needs.

When All Else Fails...

It's not realistic to believe you always have the power to influence a situation in a positive, constructive direction. There are times that no matter what you do you are not heard or responded to favorably. In rare circumstances, the child chooses to remain engulfed by fear. It has been my observation that many of these children seem to have few resources or little support from their parents or in the home environment. Perhaps they have not received encouragement in themselves and simply have no frame of reference to draw upon.

One such child who fell into this category was about six years old. She refused to cooperate with any of the hospital staff and threw unimaginable fits to draw blood and take insulin shots which, of course, were required for her very survival. I met her a few days into her hospital admission and spoke to her nurse, who told me they had to double-team her to give her the injections. She came from a socially challenging home environment and her mom, a single parent, wasn't present in the hospital that day. Four shots of insulin a day were required and it was time for another injection. The child fought with her assigned nurse and myself right from the very beginning. Despite all my experience and all that I know to do, I couldn't reach her. Her arms were flailing as

189

she was yelling, screaming and crying. We had to close the door to her room to prevent her from escaping. Sometimes boundaries come into play with these children, and if there aren't any limits set at home with either parent, then it's the same situation in a hospital environment with you. Combine that with the fear of being alone in a hospital without parental company or support, and you have a difficult situation.

What I had to help this child understand was that she had a choice in where to take the shot, but no choice in whether or not she received the shot. At this point, that had not been established. I had to physically hold her despite all her objections including my own.

As quickly as I could I gave her the injection and then looked into those tearful eyes (at eye level of course) and said, "You didn't even feel that now, did you?" My tone was more of telling her than asking her.

She didn't answer me but shook her head no and stopped crying.

"If you hold real still you won't feel them at all," I said, as she kept staring at me while continuing to give me the silent treatment.

The next day I really thought the team was getting somewhere, but we had to hold her and repeat the same routine all over again! I did all I could to ease the child's fear and kept repeating, "If you hold still, you won't feel anything."

Finally, by the following day she got the idea and for the first time pointed to where she would like to receive her injection. She no longer fought us and eventually agreed they didn't really hurt and were nothing to be scared about. Her pattern of mistrust and fear took three days and a handful of nurses to finally shift.

Don't ever label a child as incapable of any cooperation or allow your initial perception of them to be influenced by things such as:

- a known history of physical or sexual abuse by a parent even if that parent is present,
- a low socioeconomic family with limited resources or illiteracy,
- children who appear excessively spoiled or act out aggressively,
- families who seem overly sensitive or even distrustful of medical personnel, or

- families who are angry or frustrated and take it out on the medical staff at the child's expense.

Look into the individuality of each child. Believe in their innocence and in the quality of their creative spirit, despite the odds.

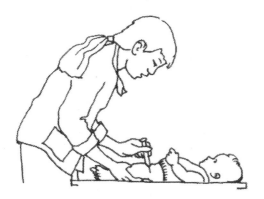

Infant "hold" for leg injection with baby on a bed or table.

Infant "hold" for leg injection in thigh with baby on your lap.

Diabetes Care for Babies, Toddlers, and Preschoolers, *1999, Jean Betschart, Reprinted with permission of John Wiley and Sons, Inc.*

"Straddle hold" to restrain arm and leg for thigh injection.

Straddle hold similar to previous hold, but showing another way to restrain arms.

Diabetes Care for Babies, Toddlers, and Preschoolers, *1999*
Jean Betschart, Reprinted with permission of John Wiley and Sons, Inc.

Thigh injection for toddler, showing arm and leg restraint.

Lap hold for arm injection, showing arm restraint.

Diabetes Care for Babies, Toddlers, and Preschoolers, *1999*
Jean Betschart, Reprinted with permission of John Wiley and Sons, Inc.

SUMMARY

1) By practicing each skill presented in this book, individually, you will begin to combine several approaches as a natural progression.

2) For an added feeling of security, have the child sit in the parent's lap when doing simple procedures.

3) Use creative distractions, take your time and don't be afraid to set boundaries to help the child work through their fear.

4) Never discount a child's ability to cooperate on at least some level, despite difficult, obvious and challenging barriers.

*When you start combining several
of the skills we have discussed,
you accelerate your effectiveness.*

"Just one great idea can completely
revolutionize your life."
–Earl Nightingale

14: Summary of Techniques

*T*he following is a list of techniques, most of which were illustrated throughout the book. Always remember, techniques in and of themselves don't work — you work the technique. The manner and spirit with which you apply them are more important than the process of the technique itself, no matter how skillfully executed. Since intention is always the place to start, we will end with always knowing that it's what takes place within you first that creates the necessary foundation upon which to build your skills. Apply these techniques with love in your heart, awareness in your mind and trust in your abilities to produce success.

Follow your intuition on what technique works best for you, in which situations you use them and which type of child you believe they're best suited for. Remember that being with the child physically is not enough, your attentive presence is also required. See the situation through the eyes of the child to increase your success with gaining cooperation and empowerment. It's more important to share yourself through a set of ideas coming from a heart space, rather than applying a structured set of learned rules in an organized fashion. Don't be technical, be loving, and watch the technique come magically alive. Through practice and a lighthearted spirit, you'll end up creating some of your own.

1. Mirror Technique.

Start with yourself and have an honest, objective look at how you physically and emotionally appear from the perspective of a frightened child. Pretend to hold a full-length mirror in front of yourself when you first enter the exam room. Try to see the total picture of the message your body language delivers by how you present yourself.

Does the child see a relaxed confidence or hesitancy in dealing with their fear and anxiety? What is the first impression you give by how you carry yourself, your physical mannerisms and the look on your face? Ask your coworkers their opinion of your initial approach. What can you learn about yourself as you observe that mirror image, and what would you change, fine-tune or adjust to get that image to work best for you and to create a milieu of confidence for the child?

2. Create a positive association with your presence.

Smile, laugh and be fun to be with. Behave as if you are the child's best friend and you're so very glad to see them. Give the child something when you first meet as a welcoming gesture. It can be anything from a crayon, to showing them a medical device or even a piece of paper with a drawing on it. A child that likes you is more willing to cooperate with you.

3. Create a nonthreatening environment.

You can do this in two ways. One is by the gentleness of your presence, approach and mannerisms and the other is by caring for the child indirectly by caring for the environment. Offer ice packs, extra pillows and warm blankets. Adjust the lighting, the temperature and the position of the bed. Tend to anything in the surroundings that helps the child understand your sole interest is their comfort level.

4. Engage the child's imagination by telling them a story.

Children love to hear stories. Once you get them a little interested, slowly start to incorporate them into the story and involve their imagination as a way of gaining cooperation. For example, a nurse and a physician once told a story to a young boy with his eyes closed about how a bunch of butterflies landed on his head and face and were kissing him. As his imagination was set into motion, they encouraged him not to move so he wouldn't scare the butterflies away. He was asked to describe the butterflies' appearance in detail and what it was like to be kissed by so many as the team worked on his scalp injuries. Another story involved a girl's favorite pet falling asleep on her chest. The child's chest was chosen in the story in order to obtain a more centralized stillness rather than just an extremity.

5. Ask the child to take on the persona of their favorite super-hero.

Find out who that hero is during your conversation with the child, and what powers this character has. Spend time talking about it. Once you have established a little rapport, play an imaginary game where they become that hero and act out the character's power during a procedure. A boy once engaged his imagination to become a cartoon superhero who had super strength in his legs while the medical team worked on his lower extremity injuries. Remember to encourage the child to give you as much detail in their mental imagery as possible to deepen the imaginative process, as well as their physical cooperation. All this is best accomplished, of course, with their eyes closed as you're actively participating in the game with them.

6. Use distraction.

Take full advantage of a child's naturally curious nature to shift their attention off of fear. Show them something that interests them: a stethoscope, a piece of equipment, a colorful Band-Aid or a coloring book. Distract the child by asking them to make a bandage for you by giving them gauze and tape. Have them open packages for you, or get them involved in some type of activity. Even just changing the conversation to something positive can give a refocusing of issues to keep their mind occupied on something other than fear.

7. Talk and interact with the child at eye level.

Most of the time this requires you as the adult to "come down" to their level while looking, talking and interacting with them. It displays attention and interest on your part and subconsciously says: we are on equal ground together. No one is bigger or smaller, more powerful or weak. We're in this together. We are a team.

8. Begin with the end in mind.

Try this technique when you're faced with a really frightened child. See into and through how they are objecting in the present moment, and envision their eventual calm cooperation through your assistance being the heart-filled, compassionate, persuasive person you are. The child may be afraid, but they haven't met you yet!

9. Say what you want, not what you don't want.

Watch your words and choose them carefully. Speak only in the positive sense, not in the negative. For example, it's better to say, "I'd like to see you *happier* about this," rather than saying, "Don't look so *sad.*" "I'll help you stay *calm,*" is better than, "Don't be *afraid.*" It's easier to keep your wording positive if you don't start your sentences with the word *don't.* Instead, start them with statements like: *You are* going to be, or *I'll* show you how to be (safe, comfortable, relaxed, etc.).

10. See the best in all children — "Hold 'em High"

See each child you work with as capable of cooperating no matter how they initially present themselves. Remember that crying, objecting and resisting are oftentimes temporary masks the child uses out of fear, and that they are very willing to trade them in for a better one once you show them how. Continue to see them as capable throughout your interaction, knowing that sometimes children will wait until the last moment to enter into their state of empowerment.

11. Match their head tilt.

To increase rapport and a feeling of being connected, tilt your head in the same direction as theirs. It shows you're paying attention to these slight details, you're in tune with them, and you want to maintain that connection.

12. Before entering a child's room visualize your physical tension leaving you.

This technique is especially important for those people who tend to hold a lot of nervous energy. Give yourself a moment of pause if you find yourself tense, stressed out from the day or the immediate situation that faces you. Don't bring that tension in the room with you. Take a moment to close your eyes, take a deep breath and with each slow exhale begin to imagine what it would look like for you to "see" that tension coming off you. For some, it evaporates like a vapor, for others it falls to the floor with a thud and goes into an imaginary hole in the ground for recycling (must have been the imagination of an environmentalist!). Show the children how to do this too or even do it together.

13. Watch your breath.

Slow, deep, relaxed abdominal breathing creates a powerful presence, especially in moments of silence. When you do speak when breathing this way your tone, pace, and volume will be a direct reflection of that calm breath. Your very presence can help to slow things down and help the child shift their attention off their fear. You will be a living, breathing example of what it's like to be calm. Children learn best by what you do, not by what you say and you're giving them something powerful to imitate despite the fact that it's subtle.

14. Listen to your intuition.

Experience in any profession helps you to get in tune with the people you serve. Getting in tune increases your understanding, and understanding leads to the ability to anticipate. When intuition comes to you and you recognize it as such, learn to listen to the message it delivers rather than discount or disregard it. Once you're good at listening to your own inner voice, get good at acting upon your instincts. By keeping in mind what is in the best interest of the people you serve, your actions will be properly guided all on their own.

15. Connect all your energy centers to your heart.

Before you start an important event or interaction, try this technique to help you to be your best. Actively and deliberately engage your imagination. Using vivid pictures in your mind, connect your mouth and all its spoken words to your heart. Connect your eyes, ears, thoughts and intelligence to your heart so all these centers originate from a space of love and heightened awareness.

Include your touch, intuition and action. Go slowly, one center at a time. Finish the mental image by seeing them all connected not just individually, but as one unified whole. You're now prepared to begin your interaction.

16. Be playful and have fun.

Relax, have fun and embrace the spirit of a child when the situation is appropriate for it. If you're confident enough in your own practiced abilities, create the appropriateness itself.

17. Intentionally create confusion for the mind to redirect negative thinking.

Confusion is a powerful method to trick the mind out of its old, worn out, repetitious, negative groove. Use confusion if it's already present or create it intentionally. Ask a fearful child to change the chair they're sitting in or even change the room you're working in along with the suggestion that if they do, they will have a better experience. Techniques such as this will momentarily cause the mind to pause in its detrimental pattern of thinking. Once you notice it's interrupted (mostly by the expression on their face and the look in their eyes), that is the precise moment to interject a positive statement or idea, and then keep repeating that statement or idea. This trick works well to first break up negative, self-destructive thinking and secondly, to give the mind an opportunity to develop a new mental loop that's more positive.

18. Drop all techniques and act from your heart.

Eliminate all techniques from your mind and forget about doing any ritual or routine whatsoever. Drop all techniques, and like an arrow, relate straight from your heart.

Afterword

Are You Ready to be a Resource for the Work?

The greatest gift we can give to each other is that of our exclusive, undivided attention. Be available to the children so totally, so full of the present moment, that you become incapable of distraction. Give the gift of yourself through offering your full attention. Share your awareness and your presence to the extent where self-protection and pretenses drop, and you can easily see the light in the eyes of each other as one. Settle in your own natural expression of who you are. As you become more and more open, receptive and true, a circle of giving and receiving of natural communication unfolds.

It is here where the greatest opportunity for a dynamic exchange awaits you and the lives you touch.

It is my sincerest wish that the spirit of working with children to transform their fear into the expression of empowerment finds its place within you. Discover that which rejoices in touching the hearts of these young innocent souls, and brings satisfaction and a sense of purpose to your work. May you find passion in all your interactions, and may that passion find you no longer afraid in the presence of children in fear. May the end of each day of challenge leave you thankful and tranquil.

I invite you to become a force of attraction, a magnet to the work where children who are afraid unknowingly find you, and your peers seek your counsel. Together, may you gravitate to each other through divine intervention, and become a resource for the work of empowerment.

I envision a day where more and more medical personnel become trained in the art of finding the playful, cooperative spirit in children despite the fear and trepidation that can exist in a medical setting. Through the compassion we fuel in each other and the loving trust expressed through the children, may the resource for this art grow and multiply.

About the Author
Rob Luka, RN, CDE, CHt

With thirty years of nursing experience, Robert Luka began his medical career in high school working as a hospital orderly. In 1977, he received an RN degree from the Millard Fillmore School of Nursing in Buffalo, NY. Since then, he has worked in intensive care, Emergency Room nursing, supervision and diabetes education. His primary interest is in working with children with experience at the Ruth and Billy Graham Children's Health Center. Currently, he works in pediatric endocrinology at the Mission Children's Reuters's Center in Asheville.

Rob is actively involved in teaching newly diagnosed children with type 1 diabetes and their families injection and blood testing skills. He speaks and consults to hospitals, and nursing and healthcare organizations on how to effectively work with frightened children in a variety of medical settings.

Living in Poona, India, in 1981 deepened and forever changed his expression of compassion in the lives of those he worked with. As a result, he has developed practical techniques that can enhance the medical experience for both patient and professional staff. His ultimate goal, through this book, is to teach empowerment to healthcare providers to create a positive experience for young, frightened patients within diverse medical settings.